PSYCHOLOGY EXPERIMENTS
ON
ANIMALS

by

Brandon Kuker-Reines

for

New England Anti-Vivisection Society

PSYCHOLOGY EXPERIMENTS ON ANIMALS
© 1982 NEW ENGLAND ANTI-VIVISECTION SOCIETY

FOREWORD

One aspect of the initial appeal and justification of the turn to non-human animals for experimentation in human psychology was the presumed simplicity of those beings and of the clinical phenomena. The present history, however, by tracing one contour of that exploitation, demonstrates the complexity and suggests the wrongheaded presumptuousness of that enterprise.

On the laboratory side, clearly we no longer see other animals as simple organisms that somehow consist of certain states such as hunger or deprivation, states readily controlled, measured, and analyzed in the laboratory setting. When we divorce these or any animals from their natural habitat and from what we now are only beginning to learn of their natural social organizations, their patterned behavior, their communication, and their various adversarial, parasitic, and reciprocal relations with their environment and other species, do we really believe we have any idea of what we have a measure?

On the clinical side, in most quarters it is no longer held that human psychopathology (even that term now gives way to the less medical and disease-tinged "disorder," "disturbance," and "problem in living") is intelligible as a disease entity, certainly not that group of infectious diseases which partially prompted the animal model research strategy. It is not a matter of infecting another species with a human disease, then to follow and eventually affect its course. Even that limited part of human psychopathology that might be attributable to constitutional or neurological defect does not express itself in physiological symptoms that are straightforward signs of a certain disease. Our disorders are not diseases so much as they are at base peculiarly human phenomena, inseparable from culture and history, from language and meaning. While limited analogies may be found on a physiological level, any analogies in the region of action, phenomenology, language, and belief are bound to be loose or bad metaphors.

We can not utilize non-human animals to study human psychopathology, not because we are not related (the thrust of contemporary understanding shows the considerable areas of convergence) but because we each have our own complexities; we each are embedded in contexts peculiar to us. For example, to seek to understand human depression in a non-human animal shorn of its habitat and thrust into the artificial world of a laboratory is bound to be ineffective, or more disconcerting, misleading.

The author has dared to enter these complexities from the inside by examining various animal models of psychopathology. Utilizing criteria fashioned by and within that enterprise, he finds them relatively unfulfilled even in their own terms. For example, he shows that most of the "major tranquillizers" which control some psychotic disorganization were discovered in human contexts, either clinical and epidemiological studies or "accidental" discovery — not in animal studies. At the same time, he documents the field's inclination to perpetuate the belief in animal research as the continued source of such findings.

This monograph begins to fill in the relative void between the development of general ethical arguments, such as what it means to speak of and to assert the rights of animals, and recent activism in the courts and in legislative assemblies which seeks to curtail and reform animal experimentation practices. Not an ethical treatise, the paper is a scholarly critical analysis and appraisal of the effectiveness of animal model research. By assessing the extent of that research's contribution to our understanding, it provides solid fuel both for the ethical debate and political action.

However, there is an ethic implicit in this work. While the thrust of contemporary ecology and ethology is to put all life over the same keel, that of the spaceship earth, this does not give us license to sacrifice our new-found crewmates to human ends. The present study argues that we ought not do so partly because we cannot effectively do so — certain human problems need remain a human affair.

Kenneth J. Shapiro, Ph.D.
Diplomate in Clinical Psychology, A.B.P.P.
Bates College
Lewiston, Maine

TABLE OF CONTENTS

INTRODUCTION

Not until late in the nineteenth century did the controversy over animal experimentation escalate to a full-blown war. The unwitting incendiary in Germany was the renowned medical scientist Robert Koch. It was Koch who dogmatized the strategy of using animals to study human disease. One of the founders of the germ theory of disease" — the belief that diseases are caused by invading microorganisms such as bacteria — Koch maintained that the only way to *prove* that a particular germ is the cause of a patient's disease is to create an "animal model of the human disease": to isolate the germ and inoculate it into a laboratory animal. If the laboratory animal contracts the disease, then and only then has it been shown scientifically that the germ was indeed the cause of the human disease. Since Koch laid down his classic postulates in the late 1800's, medical scientists have been inured with the belief that no hypothesis about a human disease can be substantiated without experimentation on an animal model of the human disease: laboratory animals that suffer from the particular human disease.

Undoubtedly, the use of animal model systems was an effective tool in the defeat of many of the major *infectious* diseases: the diseases caused by germs such as strep throat, polio and scarlet fever. During World War II, for example, the U.S. government used infected animals to "screen" for antibiotics and antimalarial drugs. Potential drugs were first tested for the ability to kill bacteria or malarial parasites *in vitro* (in the test tube) and then in animal models. It was relatively simple to create an animal model of an infectious disease. In essence, the animal's body was being used as a "living test tube." Chemicals that could kill microorganisms in animals could usually also kill them in human beings.

But today the main scourges are the chronic *noninfectious* diseases including cancer, heart disease, and stroke. Simulating these diseases in animals is a much thornier problem. Unlike the infectious diseases, the noninfectious diseases are actually a breakdown of the patient's own body. There is no discrete "germ" to isolate and inoculate in animals. For this reason, many scientists doubt the applicability of Koch's postulates to the chronic noninfectious diseases. The postulates were originally designed for diseases which have a single irreducible cause; not for diseases such as cancer which have a multi-factorial etiology. In an address delivered at the National Meeting of the American Federation for Clinical Research in 1964, Dr. Alfred Jay Bollet, associate professor of internal medicine and preventive medicine at the University of Virginia School of Medicine, said:

> Like a powerful beacon, these [Koch's] postulates guided investigation of the dread diseases of the time, and illuminated causative agents at the rate of more than a disease a year. The light shone on tuberculosis, anthrax, plague, leprosy, malaria, typhoid, diptheria, cholera, tetanus, lobar pneumonia — all within a single decade. . . .

When we seek the cause of today's major medical problems, chronic, noninfectious diseases, we receive little guidance from the Henle-Koch postulates.* Can our generation develop a new set of postulates, to help us investigate the causes of the complicated, chronic illnesses of our time?[1]

---

*"Koch's postulates" were actually first enunicated by Koch's teacher, Jacob Henle, in 1840, but medical historians have largely ignored Henle's contribution.

[1] A. J. Bollet, "On Seeking the Cause of Disease," *Clinical Research*, XII:3 (1964), pp. 305-306.

In fact, it is impossible to mimic a chronic human disease in animals. The reason is that each species is biochemically, immunologically, physiologically, and anatomically unique. The results of tests on a single strain of cancer mice cannot even be extrapolated to another strain of cancer mice — much less to the human patient. Unlike the *mathematical* models of the "exact" sciences, from which the concept of an *animal* model is derived, animal models have virtually no statistical predictive value.[2] In other words, though a treatment found effective on animals may occasionally prove useful for the human patient, it is just as likely that the treatment will prove utterly useless — if not dangerous. No amount of public relations can alter this implacable biological fact. The pioneers of the U.S. National Cancer Institute's (NCI) chemotherapy screening program recognized the problem in 1955. One of the researchers wrote:

> In the search for therapeutic agents to control microbial disease it is usually entirely feasible to isolate the offending organism from patients and to screen scores of compounds against simple *in vitro* systems. Drugs active in these experiments can then be tested for their efficacy against infections with the same organism transmitted to experimental animals. Although there are exceptions, it can be reasonably expected that a drug which has proven its value under these laboratory conditions will also have a comparable effect against the same disease in man. At the present time the investigator in cancer chemotherapy can contemplate such a reasonable procedure only with envy.[3]

Incredibly, over a quarter of a century later, the NCI has yet to uncover a single chemical that is as effective as the 10 anticancer drugs that were in use before organized cancer research even began. The 10 most effective drugs — which are capable of curing certain rare forms of cancer including childhood leukemia — were discovered not through animal experimentation as animal researchers insist, but in the way that most "wonder drugs" have been discovered: from their accidently-induced effects on human beings.[7] Testifying before the Senate Subcommittee on Investigations and Government Oversight in early 1981, the Director of Biostatistics for the prestigious Roswell Park Memorial Institute for Cancer Research, said:

> The uselessness of most of the animal model studies is less well-known. For instance, the discovery of chemotherapeutic agents for the treatment of human cancer is widely heralded as a triumph due to use of animal model systems. However, here again the exaggerated claims are coming from or are endorsed by the same people who get the federal dollars for animal research. There is little, if any, factual evidence that would support these claims. Indeed, while conflicting animal results have often delayed and hampered advances in the war on cancer, they have never produced a single substantial advance either in prevention or in the treatment of human cancer. For instance, practically all of the chemotherapeutic agents which are of value in the treatment of human cancer were found in a clinical context rather than in animal studies. The few exceptions are drugs which are inferior to or can easily be replaced by the drugs which were found in clinical studies. Because of the danger that I would tell Congress the truth

[2]S. Peller, *Quantitative Research in Human Biology and Medicine,* (Bristol: John Wright and Sons Ltd., 1967), p. 127.
[3]A. Gellhorn and E. Hirchberg, eds., "Investigation of Diverse Systems for Cancer Chemotherapy Screening," *Cancer Re-*

search, Supplement 3 (1955), p. 1.
[4]M. C. G. Israels, "Shortcomings of Animal Research in Leukaemia." In: *Ciba Foundation Symposium on Leukaemia Research,* G. E. W. Wolstenholme and M. P. Cameron, eds. (Boston: Little Brown, 1954), pp. 26-37.

about the value of animal studies, a fairly elaborate and successful effort was made by NIH (National Institute of Health) to keep me away from a meeting on this topic which was supposed to be held for the information of Congress.[5]

By far the most tenuous extension of Koch's postulates, however, is to the field of psychiatry. For nearly a century, experimental psychologists have struggled to create a true "animal model of human psychopathology." In light of the inability to model the bonafide chronic noninfectious diseases in animals, there is little hope for an animal model of the more ambiguous mental illnesses. The psychological and biological aspects of the various psychopathologies remain largely enigmatic *in human beings.* Many psychiatrists have long doubted that Koch's postulates have a place in psychiatry. Swedish psychiatrist Dr. Pér Dalen writes:

> The rules known as Koch's postulates have served as invaluable guides to the discovery of the specific causes of various infectious diseases. It may safely be assumed that their influence has also been great on the methods of study in the field of non-infectious diseases. For example, with slight modification Koch's postulates may be applied to the study of diseases caused by poisons. But can they be modified and applied with profit in psychiatric research? . . .
>
> There are, of course, close analogies between the various infectious diseases, and that is why hypotheses about their causation could successfully be tested by a standard procedure. In our field, this procedure does not yield much. . . .[6]

Notwithstanding those who claim medical science is necessarily hap-

hazard, psychiatrists needn't puzzle over the most effective strategy for elucidating at least the *biological* basis of mental illnesses (if indeed one exists). The road to medical advance is not an endlessly meandering trail. It is more like a superhighway. Medical history unmistakably reveals that the most effective strategy is logical quantitative reasoning from *human* data — clinical and epidemiological. Even in the conquest of the infectious diseases, the development of vaccines and certain antimicrobial drugs through animal research was but an addendum to the pioneering clinical and epidemiological inquiries.[7]

Today, experimental psychologists continue to drive laboratory animals "crazy", apparently heedless of the light of medical history. It will soon become apparent that the most diehard experimentalists believe that not only have they created true "animal models of human psychopathology," but that the models have led to important advances in the treatment and prevention of mental illness. Two such scientists, Drs. Gordon Gallup and Susan Suarez, of the State University of New York at Albany, recently claimed:

> . . . to imply that psychological research on animals has failed to yield important data with important implications for the treatment of human suffering is simply contrary to the facts. Significant recent developments in the treatment and understanding of such problems as phobias, obesity, drug addiction, brain disorders, ulcers, depression, enuresis, and childhood autism are tied directly or indirectly to the results of animal experimentation. . . .[8]

In support of their contention, Gallup and Suarez cite the book *Psychopathology: Experimental Models,* edited by Drs. J. D. Maser and M. E. P. Seligman.

[5]I. D. J. Bross, "How We Lost the War on Cancer," (1981).
[6]P. Dalén, "Causal Explanations in Psychiatry: A Critique of Some Current Concepts," *British Journal of Psychiatry,* 115 (1969), pp. 129 & 132.
[7]Peller, pp. 1-403.
[8]G. Gallup and S. Suarez, "On the Use of Animals in Psychological Research," *The Psychological Record,* 30 (1980), p. 212.

Not only will it become clear that the animal models presented in the Maser/Seligman text have failed to make inroads against a single mental illness, but that they don't even come close to meeting the experimentalists' own criteria for a valid animal model. The uselessness of animal research and the extraordinary potential of harmlessly studying human beings is borne out not just by medical history, but by the history of psychology.

THE ROOTS OF EXPERIMENTAL PSYCHOLOGY ON ANIMALS

PAVLOV AND THE CONDITIONED REFLEX

One of the major figures in the founding of experimental psychology on animals is the early twentieth-century Russian physiologist Ivan Pavlov. The form of learning known as "classical conditioning" was defined by Pavlov's Nobel-prize-winning studies of the salivary reflex in dogs. Pavlov investigated how long it takes a dog to associate the sound of a buzzer with feeding time. By means of a small incision, Pavlov made an opening in the dog's cheek through which a glass tube was inserted into the opening of one of the salivary glands. The saliva which dripped from the tube was collected and measured in finely-graduated containers. Since the salivary reflex is so easily disturbed, Pavlov took every precaution to guard against outside interference. The experiments were conducted in specially-built windowless, sound-proof rooms with walls made of turf two feet thick. Both the food (meatpaste) and the substitute stimuli (buzzers) were presented automatically. Pavlov watched the dog through a periscope in the wall.

To train the dogs to salivate at the sound of a tone, Pavlov first presented both the meat paste and the sound of the buzzer at nearly the same time. The dogs began to salivate, of course, because of the meat paste: the so-called unconditioned stimulus (the stimulus that naturally causes animals to salivate). The dog has still to learn to associate the buzzer — the "conditioned" or "artificial stimulus" — with food. Eventually, however, the dogs learned that the buzzer signalled that food was soon to come. So they began to salivate at the sound of the tone alone. By measuring the amount of saliva in the containers, Pavlov could determine precisely how long it took the dogs to become conditioned: to learn to salivate at the sound of the tone.

The use of animals in American experimental psychology began chiefly as a reaction to Freud and other introspectionists.[9] While Freud formulated his theories through introspection — delving into his own mind and that of others — a number of early experimental psychologists were dissatisfied with the vagaries of psychoanalytic theory. Some American experimental psychologists were anxious to find any technique that might establish psychology as a true natural science. Such experimentalists seized upon Pavlov's principle of classical conditioning as the basis of an entirely new approach to human psychology. Famed experimental psychologist John B. Watson believed that psychology should only concern itself with the objective analysis of outwardly observable behaviors. In 1916, he announced to the world the strategy he called "behaviorism."

It is hardly a surprise that some of the early behaviorists chose as the focus of their research not human behavior but the behavior of animals. Koch's postulates had long dominated virtually every aspect of medical research; for a young discipline, eager to establish itself as a bonafide natural science, no undertaking could promise to lend a more immediate aura of respectability than animal experimentation. The most famous names in experimental psychology — Skinner, Thorndike, Watson, Tolman, Guthrie, Hull, and Spence — all formulated their theories through intensive animal (primarily rat) research.

During this Golden Age of Rat Research (1930-1950), the experimentalists' were convinced that animal experiments would lead unflinchingly to the conquest of mankind's greatest social problems. The great experimental psychologists of the period said so in no uncertain terms. Dr. Edward C. Tolman wrote in 1938:

> Let me close now with a final confession of faith. I believe that everything important in psychology (except perhaps such matters as the building up of a superego, that is everything save such matters as involve society and words) can be investigated in essence through the continued experimental and theoretical analysis of the determiners of rat behavior at a choice point in a maze. Herein I believe I agree with Professor Hull and also with Professor Thorndike. . . .[10]

A few years later, in 1943, Dr. Clark L. Hull, found even greater cause for optimism. He believed rat experiments were directly relevant to:

> . . . the theory of skills and their acquisition; of communicational symbolism or language (semantics); of the use of symbolism in individual problem solution involving thought and reasoning; of social or ritualistic symbolism; of economic values and valuation; of moral values and valuation; of aesthetic values and valuation; of familial behavior; of individual adaptive efficiency (intelligence); of the formal educative processes; of psychogenic disorders; of social control and delinquency; of character and personality; of culture and acculturation; of matic and religious practices; of custom, law, and jurisprudence; of politics and government; and of many other

[9]C. S. Hall and G. Lindzey, *Theories of Personality,* (New York: John Wiley & Sons, Inc., 1970), p. 418.

[10]E. C. Tolman, "The Determiners of Behavior at a Choice Point," *Psychological Review,* 45 (1938), p. 34.

specialized behavior fields....[11]

Today, experimental psychologists are not so grandiose in their expectations of animal research. They are content to concede that rat research will never elucidate the basic nature of economic systems, for example. Yet they continue to insist that animal experiments are the key to defeating mental illness.

PAVLOVIAN "EXPERIMENTAL NEUROSIS"

Under the spell of Koch's Postulates, Pavlov himself believed it possible to simulate psychopathology in animals. During his work on the conditioned reflex in dogs, two dramatic accidents occurred that convinced him to devote the last decade of his life to applying conditioning principles to psychiatric illness. The first incident was an unexpected "neurotic breakdown" in a dog involved in the famous circle-ellipse experiment of Shenger-Krestovnikova in 1921. The experiment unfolded as follows:

A circle was repeatedly projected onto a screen in front of the dog. Each time the dog saw the circle on the screen he would be given food until he learned to associate the circle with food. Once salivation to the circle alone became well-established, the experimenters presented an ellipse that was twice as long as wide, but this time without food. The dog soon stopped salivating at the sight of the ellipse. But then the experimenters made the dog's ability to discrimate more difficult by changing the ratio of the axes of the ellipse so that it looked more and more like the circle. The dog was doing fine until the ratio of axes reached 9:8, when the dog's discrimination broke down and he began squealing, and destroyed the experimental apparatus. While the dog had previously gone willingly each day into the experimental room, he barked violently and resisted entering the room.

The second incident was even more dramatic. During the Leningrad flood of 1924, the building that housed Pavlov's dogs was flooded. The dogs were trapped in a building slowly filling with

[11]C. L. Hull, *Principles of Behavior: An Introduction to Behavior Theory* (New York: Appleton-Century-Crofts, 1943), p. 399.

water. It rose until the dogs were swimming around with their heads barely above water at the tops of the cages. Luckily, at the last second, a laboratory attendant pulled the dogs to safety. When Pavlov resumed his conditioning experiments, he found that the dogs' conditioned reflexes were poor. After the dogs' reflexes appeared restored, Pavlov let a trickle of water run in under the door of the laboratory. The dogs became so terrified that their condition-ed reflexes once again became impaired. Pavlov believed that both accidents had induced a state of "experimental neuroses" in the dogs, which might be similar to the neuroses of human beings. So, at the age of 80, he decided to enter the field of psychological research. He thought perhaps research on animals rendered ill through experimentation might shed light on the causes, mechanism and treatment of human psychopathology.

PAVLOVIAN "EXPERIMENTAL SCHIZOPHRENIA"

Once Pavlov became interested in the similarities between animal and human behavior he began to make regular visits to the psychiatric hospital near Leningrad to observe schizophrenic patients. Certain symptoms piqued his interest: apathy, dullness, immobility, stereotypy, and negativism on the one hand, and playfullness, unconventionality and childish behavior on the other. Immediately, he was reminded of his dogs under the influence of hypnosis. By hypnosis, Pavlov meant an intermediate state between being awake and asleep. Pavlov hypnotized his dogs by repeatedly presenting the same stimulus (as the swinging gold watch in human hypnosis).

Pavlov had noticed that in the early phases of laboratory hypnosis the dogs lost their reactions to strong stimuli but continued to react to the weak stimuli. He believed this laboratory phenomenon had an analogue in the clinic: a schizophrenic patient might respond only to whispered questions. One of the most extreme symptoms of schizophrenia — stereotypic repetition of the same movements — also appeared to have an analogue in hypnotized dogs. Most alert dogs habitually licked the front of their bodies and paws during a food experiment. Early in hypnosis, the licking was greatly prolonged. Thus Pavlov believed the hypnotized dog might be an animal model of schizophrenia. The idea of an animal model of human psychopathology was born.

CRITIQUE OF ANIMAL MODELS OF PSYCHOPATHOLOGY

INTRODUCTION

Over a half century since Pavlov drew the first comparisons between abnormal animal behavior and human mental illness, experimental psychologists continue to attempt to simulate mental diseases in animals. In the true behaviorist tradition of John B. Watson, the experimentalists are still trying to create animal models of psychopathology by imitating the symptoms of the syndromes in human beings. Yet psychologists are not even sure of what behaviors comprise the "core symptoms" of each type of mental illness in people: animal researchers have a difficult time figuring out what to imitate. It is evident that no progress against psychopathology will be made until psychologists get a clearer picture of the actual human conditions. In an effort to impress this

inescapable reality on experimental psychologists at a recent symposium on animal models in human psychobiology, Clinical Psychopharmacologist Dr. Dennis L. Murphy of the National Institute of Mental Health, said:

> The main point at issue here is that in some ways, studies of these disorders, including even simple behavioral phenomenology, is still just beginning. It is not surprising that there is some resistance to animal models for these disorders when even the symptomatology, to say nothing of the etiology of these states, is only partly known. There is actually a great need for much more careful study of the simple behavioral phenomenology of these disorders. In fact, it has

recently been suggested by a British MRC clinical study unit in Edinburgh that some of the behavioral phenomena observed and rated in animal lesion and drug studies might be evaluated and rated in patients. Phenomena akin to stereotypic activity, exploratory behavior, and aggressive-submissive behavior occur in somewhat altered form in patients, but, in fact, have not yet been subjected to systematic observation and documentation in man. Animal model buildng may well be outracing knowledge of the phenomena to be observed in natural human states.[12]

Not only will it soon be shown that no clinical advances have arisen from the past 50 years of taxpayer-supported animal research, but that the current animal models do not even come close to meeting the criteria for valid animal models enunciated by the experimental psychologists McKinney and Bunney in 1969.[13] The criteria specify that the animal model and the human mental illness must have similar (1) causes, (2) symptoms, (3) response to treatments that are effective in the clinical illness, and (4) neurobiological mechanism. A model-by-model critique primarily of the animal models presented in the book *Psychopathology: Experimental Models* follows; criterion (4) will be dealt with at the end of the chapter. The most cursory examination of the following gallery of animal models is a journey into a macabre never-never land bordering on the comic.

[12]D. L. Murphy, "Animal Models for Human Psychopathology: Observations from the Vantage Point of Clinical Psychopharmacology," In: *Animal Models in Human Psychobiology,* G. Serban and A. Kling, eds., (New York: Plenum Press, 1976), p. 268.

[13]W. T. McKinney, Jr. and W. E. Bunney, Jr., "Animal Model of Depression," *Archives of General Psychiatry,* 21 (1969), p. 246.

SCHIZOPHRENIA

"I remember very well the day it happened. We were staying in the country and I had gone for a walk alone as I did now and then. Suddenly, as I was passing the school, I heard a German song; the children were having a singing lesson. I stopped to listen, and at that instant a strange feeling came over me, a feeling hard to analyze but akin to something I was to know too well later — a disturbing sense of unreality. It seemed to me that I no longer recognized the school, it had become as large as a barracks; the singing children were prisoners, compelled to sing. It was as though the school and the children's song were set apart from the rest of the world. At the same time my eye encountered a field of wheat whose limits I could not see. The yellow vastness, dazzling in the sun, bound up with the song of the children imprisoned in the smooth stone school-barracks, filled me with such anxiety that I broke into sobs. I ran home to our garden and began to play 'to make things seem as they usually were,' that is, to return to reality. It was the first appearance of those elements which were always present in later sensations of unreality; illimitable vastness, brilliant light, and the gloss and smoothness of material things. I have no explanation for what happened, or why. But it was during this same period that I learned my father had a mistress and that he made my mother cry. This revelation bowled me over because I had heard my mother say that if my father left her, she would kill herself."

— Autobiography of a Schizophrenic Girl, P-1.

MODEL 1: CONDITIONED-AVOIDANCE RESPONSE (CAR)

The most common animal model of human schizophrenia is the "Conditioned Avoidance Response Model." It is widely used by pharmaceutical firms for testing potential anti-psychotic drugs. The animal model is developed by conditioning the animal to press a lever whenever a bell is sounded in order to avoid receiving an electric shock. Any drug that causes the animal to ignore the bell and receive the electric shock is suspected to have antipsychotic properties.[14]

Criterion 1: No one has yet argued that CAR mimics the etiology of human schizophrenia.

Criterion 2: No one has yet argued that the symptoms of CAR animals mimic schizophrenia.

Criterion 3: Though the antipsychotic drug chlorpromazine (CPZ) does reduce lever-pressing in rats, this fact can hardly be taken to validate the model. The underlying rationale of the model is that true antipsychotic drugs will make the animal less afraid of the impending shock; the animal will fail to press the lever to avoid shock. However, in experiments in which the bell signals impending food pellets and *not* electric shock, chlorpromazine also causes rats to fail to lever-press for food pellets.[15] The contention that the effective drugs make animals less afraid is contradicted. Instead, it seems that chlorproma-zine acts as a general depressant in animals, and all types of responding are reduced.

Drs. Steven Matthysse and Susan Haber established four criteria for evaluating the similarity in response to known effective antipsychotic drugs between animal models and schizophrenics. Of the four criteria (1. potency correlation, 2. absence of influence by nonantipsychotic drugs, 3. absence of building tolerance, and 4. absence of anticholinergic blockade), only the first criteria came close to being met: potency.[16] Yet the potency correlation held for only one species — the rat. Even in this single species, however, the antipsychotic thioridazine was found to be less active in suppressing contioned avoidance in the rat than would be expected from its clinical potency.[17] In addition, while the drugs thioridazine and CPZ are approximately equal in potency in the clinic, in another form of CAR — "discrete pole-climbing avoidance" — in rats, thioridazine was reported to be approximately one-fifth to one fifteenth the potency of CPZ.[18]

CLINICAL IMPACT

No useful antipsychotic drugs — drugs that are used to treat psychoses such as schizophrenia and depression — have been discovered through the CAR or any other animal model. The anti-psychotics in current use were

[14]C. Kornetsky and C. Markowitz, "Animal Models and Schizophrenia." In: *Model Systems in Biological Psychiatry,* D. Ingle and H. Shein, eds. (Cambridge, MA: The MIT Press, 1975), p. 27.

[15]J. J. Boren, "The Study of Drugs With Operant Techniques," In: *Operant Behavior: Areas of Research and Application,* W. Honig, ed., (New York: Appleton-Century-Crofts, 1966), pp. 677-717.

[16]S. Mattysse and S. Haber, "Animal Models of Schizophrenia," In: *Model Systems in Biological Psychiatry,* D. Ingle and H. Shein, eds. (Cambridge, MA: The MIT Press, 1975), p. 7

[17]E. A. Swinyard, H. H. Wolf, G. B. Fink and L. S. Goodman, "Some Neuropharmacological Properties of Thioridazine Hydrochloride (Mellaril)," *Journal of Pharmacology and Experimental Therapeutics,* 126 1959), pp. 312-317.

[18]*Ibid.,* p. 315.

found from their effects on human beings. There are four classes of antipsychotic drugs: (1) Phenothiazines (Chloromazine), (2) *Rauwolfia* alkaloids (Reserpine), (3) MAO-inhibitors (Iproniazid) and (4) Tricyclic compounds (Imipramine).

The phenothiazines, like so many other wonder drugs, were discovered by an alert clinician who was using the drugs for a completely different purpose but noted interesting side-effects. In the late nineteenth and early twentieth century, phenothiazine was used clinically as an antibiotic. In the late 1930's, a phenothiazine derivative, promethazine was noted to have antihistaminic and sedative properties in patients being treated for infectious diseases. The phenothiazine drug chlorpromazine was initially developed to be used as a sedative. The French surgeon H. Laborii first used it as a preanesthetic sedative, but was struck by the odd effects it had on patients: they maintained consciousness but were almost completely indifferent to their surroundings. In 1951-52 in Paris, several psychiatrists noted the ability of the new agent to increase the effectiveness of barbituates in sedating manic and other psychotic patients. Finally, in 1952-53, Drs. J. Delay and P. Deniker found chlorpromazine highly effective alone in treating their psychiatric patients in Paris.[19]

The *Rauwolfia* alkaloid drug called Reserpine was discovered in almost precisely the same way, also in the mid-1950's. Originally used to treat high blood pressure, it was found that Reserpine often produced a syndrome in patients almost indistinguishable from clinical depression; and it was then used to treat schizophrenia.[20]

The MAO-inhibiting drug Iproniazid was originally used to treat tuberculosis. The drug often seemed to cause euphoric effects that were highly reminiscent of schizophrenia; and was then used to treat depression.[21]

Since the 1940's, it was well-known that the Tricyclic compound Imipramine had antihistaminic and sedative properties in human beings. Because of the similarity between the effects of Imipramine and the known-effective antipsychotic Chlorpromaxine, Swiss psychiatrists tried Imipramine in clinical trials in 1957-58. It was shown to have marked mood-elevating and behavior-activating properties. The drug is effective in certain forms of depression.[22]

Ironically, the most effective antipsychotic drugs would likely have been discarded if they were first tested on animals. In the U. S. Public Health Service study *Establishing the Efficacy of Psychotropic Agents,* the editors write:

> During the brief history of treating psychiatric depressed patients with drugs, therapeutic efficacy has almost always been developed from clinical experience — usually by accident. For example, there is little in the available animal models of iproniazid or imipramine to suggest their possible usefulness in depressed patients. The then existing criterion for predicting clinical antidepressant action was that the compound increased the gross psychomotor activities of animals, a criterion derived from experience with the amphetamines and embodying the classical neuro-pharmacological model of excitation versus depression as a single bipolar dimension of CNS action. By this criterion, neither imipramine nor iproniazid was predicted to be antidepressant. . . .[23]

[19]R. J. Baldessarini, *Chemotherapy in Psychiatry* (Cambridge, MA: Harvard University Press. 1977). p. 13.

[20]J. W. Maas, "Clinical Biochemistry and the Choice of the Appropriate Medication for the Psychiatric Patient," In: *The Psychobiology of Depression,* J. Mendels, ed. (New York: Spectrum Publishing, 1975), p. 1

[21]*Ibid.*

[22]Baldessarini, p. 77.

[23]J. Levine, B. Schield, L. Bouthilet, Eds., *Establishing the Efficacy of Psychotropic Agents* (P.H.S. Publication No. 2138, 1971), p. 101.

Many psychiatrists doubt that the animal models — including CAR and the models used for drug screening — hold the slightest similarity to true mental illness. Dr. R. J. Baldessarini writes:

> The behavioral effects of drugs in the experimental situation are often very different from the effects observed clinically. An outstanding example of this phenomenon is that large acute doses of most antidepressants tend to produce sedation in normal laboratory animals, and it has been very difficult to devise reliable laboratory behavioral tests to screen potential new antidepressant drugs. Another problem is that most of the so-called 'animal models of affective (mental) illness' are more nearly models of sedation or stimulation, thus making it very tricky to make predictions about human clinical responses based on animal behavior. . . .[24]

MODEL 2: HALLUCINOGENIC DRUGS

Another animal model of schizophrenia is created by injecting laboratory animals with hallucinogenic drugs such as LSD, mescaline and amphetamine.[25] The symptoms of animals that are "high" on mescaline or LSD differ so sharply from the symptoms displayed when an animal is intoxicated by amphetamine that many scientists consider the two drugged states completely different models.

Criterion 1: The original rationale for creating hallucinogenic drug models of schizophrenia was that it was thought that schizophrenia was caused by a natural hallucinogenic chemical in the bloodstream.[26-27] Today, few scientists believe schizophrenia is caused by natural hallucinogens.[28-30] One of the primary rationales for making animal models of schizophrenia with hallucinogenic drugs has thus been debunked.

[24]R. J. Baldessarini, "Amine Hypotheses in Effective Illness," In: *The Psychobiology of Depression,* J. Mendels, Ed. (New York: Spectrum Publishing, 1975), p. 74.

[25]G. Ellison, J. Ring, D. Ross and B. Axelrod, "Cumulative Alterations in Rat Behavior During Continuous Administration of LSD or Mescaline: Absence of Tolerance?" *Biological Psychiatry,* 15 (1980), pp. 95-99.

[26]Fr. Franzen and H. Goss, "Tryptamine, N, N-dimethyltryptamine, N, N-dimethyl-5-hydroxytryptamine and 5-methoxytryptamine in Human Blood and Urine," *Nature,* 206 (1965), p. 1052.

[27]R. Greenberg, "N, N-Dimethylated and N, N-diethylated Indoleamines in Schizophrenia," In: *Chemical Modulation of Brain Function — A Tribute to J. E. P. Toman,* H. C. Savelli, ed. (New York: Raven Press, 1973), pp. 277-296.

[28]L. R. Mandel, A. Rosegay, R. W. Walker, W. J. A. Vanden-Heuvel, and J. Rokach, "5-Methyltetrahydrofolate Acid as a Mediator in the Formation of Pyriodoindoles," *Science,* 186 (1974), pp. 741-743.

[29]T. G. Bidder, L. R. Mandel, H. S. Ahn, R. W. Walker and W. J. A. VandenHeuvel, "Blood and Urinary DMT Concentrations in Acute Psychotic Disorders," *Lancet,* 1 (1974), p. 165.

[30]J. Lipinski, L. R. Mandel, H. S. Ahn, W. J. A. VandenHeuvel, and R. W. Walker, "Blood Dimethyltryptamine Concentrations in Psychotic Disorders," *Biological Psychiatry,* 9:1 (1974), pp. 89-91.

Criterion 2: Competent psychiatrists can easily distinguish between human beings on an "LSD trip" and true schizophrenia. Hallucinogenic drugs given to normal volunteers cannot even mimic schizophrenia in human beings much less in animals. Dr. I. Feinberg compared the hallucinations of schizophrenics with those of normal people given LSD. He found that while the hallucinations induced by LSD were primarily visual, those of the schizophrenics were primarily auditory. The schizophrenics heard "voices." Even when schizophrenics experienced visual hallucinations, they were very different from the LSD-induced hallucinations. Certain mental images such as lattice-work, cobwebs, tunnels, alleys and spirals were invariably reported by LSD volunteers but never by schizophrenics.[31]

Dr. L. E. Hollister also contends that psychedelic drugs do not mimic schizophrenia. In a well-controlled study, he asked a group of psychiatrists to listen to tape-recorded interviews with both LSD volunteers and true schizophrenics. The psychiatrist concluded that the primary difference was that drugged subjects experienced a defect in perception while the schizophrenics had disturbances in their thought.[32]

Yet another critic of the drug model, Dr. S. H. Snyder, found that LSD given to schizophrenics did not worsen their condition as would be expected. The drug produced the typical psychedelic effects that the volunteers had experienced. The patients themselves were aware of the differences between the drug's effects and their own mental condition.[33]

During a symposium of the New York Academy of Sciences on the biology of schizophrenia in 1962, Dr. Hollister concluded:

> The term "model psychosis" has been misleading in implying an actual model of schizophrenic reactions. This notion is comforting to all kinds of investigators. For the clinician it provides a way to turn the model psychosis on and off more or less at will and do this repetitively to study whichever parameters appeal to his interest. The animal researcher is also able to study an illness to which, so far as one can tell, all except humans are immune. Isolated tissues may be used: a theory of schizophrenia may be based on the behavior of a strip of rat uterus bathed in serotonin with or without added LSD-25. Even isolated enzyme systems may be studied: a number of reports indicated that LSD-25 has a strong inhibitory action on human serum pseudocholinesterase *in vitro.* I have been unable to demonstrate any effect on serum pseudocholinesterase activity in subjects given psychotomimetic drugs. . . . Thus it is easy to be led into the fallacy that generalizations pertinent to schizophrenic reactions can be based on work with psychotomimetic drugs or that it is highly relevant to the clinical problem.[34]

Though the animal model created by amphetamine injection exhibits a form of stereotypy — constant repetition of certain movements — that is superficially similar to the stereotypy of paranoid schizophrenics, the animal symptoms are still vastly different from schizophrenia in human beings. Even in people, amphetamine psychosis and schizophrenia have very different clinical manifestations. For example, visual hallucinations are much more frequent

[31] I. Feinberg, "A Comparison of the Visual Hallucinations in Schizophrenics With Those Induced by Mescaline and LSD-25." In: *Hallucinations,* L. J. West, ed., (New York: Grune and Stratton, 1962).

[32] L. E. Hollister, "Drug-induced Psychoses and Schizophrenic Reactions: A Critical Comparison," *Annals of the New York Academy of Sciences,* 96 (1962), pp. 80-89.

[33] S. H. Snyder, "Catecholamines as Mediators of Drug Effects in Schizophrenia." In: *The Neurosciences Third Study Program,* F. O. Schmitt and F. G. Worden, eds. (Cambridge, MA: The MIT Press, 1974) pp. 721-732.

[34] Hollister, p. 87.

among amphetamine users than schizophrenics. The amphetamine tends to make its users want to move about more than most schizophrenics (i.e., psychomotor stimulation is greater in amphetamine psychosis). In addition, the many *nonparanoid* symptoms of schizophrenia such as "flattened affect" (unresponsiveness) and "looseness of associations" (tendency for the mind to wander) are entirely absent from the amphetamine-induced state even in human beings.[35]

Criterion 3: Drs. S. Matthysse and S. Haber scrutinized the literature on animal models of schizophrenia via amphetamine and found that of the four criteria that they had established for determining the similarity of effects of known antipsychotic drugs on animal models and human schizophrenics, *not a single criterion was met.*[36]

CLINICAL IMPACT

No new forms of treatment or prevention of schizophrenia have arisen from this model.

MODEL 3: REWARD-APPRECIATION DEFICIT

Based on the theory that schizophrenics cannot appreciate rewards, Drs. L. Stein and C. Wise devised an "animal reward-appreciation deficit model."

Stein and Wise postulate that schizophrenics cannot appreciate rewards because they are missing the enzyme that protects the region of the brain that is

[35]D. S. Bell, "Comparison of Amphetamine Psychosis and Schizophrenia," *British Journal of Psychiatry,* 111 (1965), pp. 701-707.

[36]Matthysse and Haber, p. 7.

responsible for appreciating rewards (medial forebrain bundle). Without the critical enzyme, they maintain, a highly toxic substance (6-Hydroxydopamine) builds up and destroys the nerves in the "reward region" of the brain. To create the animal model, they injected 6-hydroxydopamine directly into the brains of experimental animals. They also wired the "reward region" of the animals' brains with electrodes, which were hooked up to a lever in the animals' cages. So the animals could stimulate their own "reward region" (i.e. they could reward themselves) simply by pressing the lever. After 6-hydroxydomamine injection, the animals "rewarded themselves" less often, which Stein and Wise interpreted to reflect damage in the "reward pathways" — thus mimicking the ostensible behavior problem in true schizophrenia.[37]

Criterion 1: There is at present no evidence that human schizophrenics suffer from an excess of 6-hydroxydopamine. The authors do not deny this.

Criterion 2: (A.) The model deals with only one symptom — inability to appreciate rewards — out of many symptoms that have been postulated to comprise the disorder called schizophrenia. Even the authors' choice of that single symptom is based on but a single theory out of many theories of the fundamental symptoms of schizophrenia. Bleuler, in his seminal account, and Meehl, a more contemporary theorist, both maintain that the fundamental symptoms of schizophrenia are:

1) disturbance of association (inability to link concepts)
2) disturbance of affectivity (abnormal emotionality)
3) preference for fantasy over reality
4) inclination to divorce oneself from reality (autism)

Stein and Wise never *explicitly* rationalize choosing to study only the symptom called anhedonia: inability to appreciate rewards. In reply to scientists who had criticized the limited similarity between the symptoms of the animal model and schizophrenia, Stein and Wise would only *implicitly* rationalize their choice of anhedonia by implying that it is the fundamental cause of symptoms 1) and 2), which in turn result in symptoms 3)-5). The authors wrote:

> According to Bleuler and Meehl, the fourth fundamental symptom, ambivalence, like autism, may be derived from disturbances in the 'elementary' or 'simple' functions of association and affectivity. Hence, we felt it would be consistent with Bleuler's concept of schizophrenia to focus attention on these functions. (Emphasis added.)[40]

In reality, however, Stein and Wise' rationale for studying anhedonia has little to do with Bleuler's theory of schizophrenia. As the authors themselves state concerning the cause of symptom 1), Bleuler says only that "schizophrenic associations lose their continuity because the thoughts are not related and directed by any unifying concept of purpose or goal.' "[41] He does *not* say or even imply, however, that the schizophrenic's lack of goals is a result of an inability to appreciate rewards. Concerning the cause of symptom 2) (the lack of emotion that many schizophrenics display), Stein and Wise do not cite Bleuler at all. They refer instead to Rado. Rado is in fact the only theorist cited who directly states that schizophrenia has anything to do with the inability to appreciate rewards. Stein and Wise write: "In Rado's view, the disturbance of affect stems from the fact that

[37]L. Stein and C. Weiss, "Possible Etiology of Schizophrenia: Progressive Damage of the Noradrenergic Reward Mechanism by Endogenous 6-Hydroxydopamine," *Science,* 171 (1971), pp. 1032-1034.

[38]E. Bleuler, *Dementia Praecox or the Group of Schizophrenias* (New York: International Universities Press, 1950), pp. 53 & 63.

[39]P. E. Meehl, *American Psychologist,* 17 (1962), p. 827.

[40]L. Stein and C. Weiss, Letter to the Editor, *Science,* 175 (1972), p. 923.

[41]Stein and Wise, "Possible Etiology," p. 1032.

the 'pleasure resources are inherently deficient.' "[42] Even Rado, however, does not contend that the "reward-appreciation" deficit causes anything but the disturbance in affectivity seen in schizophrenics (symptom 2). Two critics of the Reward-Appreciation Deficit Model wrote:

> Stein and Wise mentioned Rado's view that pleasure resources are inherently deficient in schizophrenia. This concept, which was elaborated by Meehl and termed anhedonia, appears to be most germane to the hypothesis of Stein and Wise . . . In relating their findings to schizophrenia, they might better have limited themselves to trying to explain some of the characteristics of that disorder, such as anhedonia, rather than to explain the entire disorder, which includes other characteristics their findings do not explain.[43]

(B.) It is in fact highly questionable that injection of 6-hydroxydomamine actually caused the animals to have less appreciation for rewards. There is evidence that the animals "rewarded themselves" less often because the drug merely lowers the animals' level of arousal, not because the drug decreases their ability to appreciate rewards. If experimenters themselves electrically stimuate the animals' brains the day following administration of 6-hydroxydopamine — to "wake them up" — then there is no decrease in the frequency with which the animals stimulate their own reward centers. Two other critics of the Stein-Wise model actually performed this experiemnt and concluded:

> It is our contention that Stein and Wise would not have obtained even a temporary decrement in the rate of self stimulation after 6-HDA had they given their animals priming simulation. . . .[44]

Criterion 3: Stein and Wise tested only one antipsychotic drug on their animal model: chlorpromazine. While the drug appears to increase the animals' frequency of self-rewarding, this fact can hardly be held to verify the Stein-Wise model because it actually contradicts their theory at a basic biological level. One of the biological actions of chlorpromazine in animals is to block the nerve receptors that "catch" nerve transmitters such as dopamine and norepinephrine. Under the Stein and Wise theory, these nerve transmitters are critical for maintaining normal reward appreciation activity. Theoretically, then, chlorpromazine should *inhibit* self-stimulatory activity. Yet, in fact, the Stein-Wise study shows clearly that chlorpromazine. *increases* self-stimulation. The same critics continue:

> It is surprising, however, that in the data by Stein and Wise . . . there appears to be evidence for maintenance and even potentiation of self-stimulation rates under chlorpromazine, although data in the literature, as well as the theory of Stein and Wise, should predict a suppressive effect, because one of the reported actions of chlorpromazine is to block adrenergic receptor sites.[45]

[42]*Ibid.*
[43]J. S. Strauss and W. T. Carpenter, Letter to the Editor, *Science,* 175 (1972), p. 921.
[44]S. Antelman, A. S. Lippa and A. E. Fisher, Letter to the Editor, *Science,* 175 (1972), p. 919.
[45]*Ibid.,* p. 920

To date, no methods of treatment or prevention have arisen from the Reward-Appreciation Deficit Animal Model of Stein and Wise. In fact, the prevailing opinion among experimental psychologists is that it is unlikey that there will ever be a true animal model of schizophrenia:

"The validity of any experimental model of human psychopathology will naturally depend on the similarities between the model itself and the clinical disorder. For this reason the difficulties inherent in defining schizophrenia as a unitary disorder, or in simply identifying core symptoms, will undoubtedly continue to plague future attempts at developing such a model. At the present time we could safely surmise that there is *no* adequate experimental model for schizophrenia in that there is no known experimental procedure that can reproduce even a small percentage of what we now believe composes the schizophrenic syndrome. . . .[46]

"The afternoon discussants seem to agree that with respect to certain human illnesses, e.g., epilepsy, depression, hyperactivity, or symptoms related to observable motor abnormalities, animal models may be quite pertinent and in some cases, have already been quite useful. However, the development and relevance of animal models of schizophrenia remains controversial and no clear evidence for such a model has yet emerged. Dr. Delgado and others have argued that schizophrenia is a distinctly human illness, manifested by disturbances in thinking, affect, verbal communications, interpersonal relations and, in many cases, hallu-

cinations — none of which can be effectively studied in animals despite our ability to alter their brain chemistry, rearing conditions or social environment setting. Perhaps, as suggested by Dr. Delgado and seconded by Dr. Corson and Dr. Serban, animals do not have the same components in the cerebral cortex that might be responsible for the mediation of "schizophrenic" symptoms.[47]

Direct animal models have been developed for many human disease states such as hypertension, cancer, and diabetes. Using such models, researchers have been able to uncover much information concerning the underlying mechanisms of these disease states. This has been possible because in these cases the close similarities between the animal and human states have fostered an assurance that the researcher's experimental manipulations will have a direct parallel in man. In the field of mental illness we are not quite so fortunate. It is possible, as the terminology implies that mental illness is a uniquely human disorder. With schizophrenia, unlike those diseases mentioned above, it is often difficult to determine the particular variables that define the disease. Certain animals can be made to behave in a manner that appears to the human observer to be depressed, anxious, fearful, or aggressive. In some cases, however, these decriptions may be more in the eye of the beholder than in the brain of the animal, for we don't often tend to attribute our own human experience to animals. Conversely, certain types of behavior may be so

[46]S. M. Paul, "Models of Madness: Animal Models of Schizophrenia," In: *Psychopathology: Experimental Models*, J. D. Maser and M. E. P. Seligman, eds. (San Francisco: W. H. Freeman and Co., 1977), p. 384.

[47]G. Serban and A. Kling, *Animal Models in Human Psychobiology*, (New York: Plenum Press, 1976), p. 273.

uniquely human that they cannot be meaningfully replicated in animals. Could we, for example, develop an animal model for dishonesty?[48]

[48]Kornetsky and Markowitz, p. 26.

DEPRESSION

"I told you of my feeling about Rembrandt: of how his pictures to this day possess a menacing quality, a gloomy depressing quality. I used to sit at home tears streaming (I wept more then, I am sure, than in the whole of my childhood) desperately trying to distract myself from the hellish state of seemingly perpetual misery I lived in with music and books. Perhaps I was drawn to Rembrandt by the strongly religious content of his work — and especially perhaps by the depiction of Jesus's sufferings. The guilt and atonement attracted me morbidly, I am sure. Music was the greatest comfort, but I could not endure light, happy music. I derived what can be called a truly cathartic support from music that expressed a mood in sympathy with my own. It sounds, I know, like a neurotic self-torture, but I assure you that it kept me going. At that time ordinary objects — chairs, tables and the like — possessed a frightening, menacing quality which is very hard to describe vividly in the way that I was then affected. It was as though I lived in some kind of hell containing nothing from which I could obtain relief or comfort. My wife was wonderfully supporting but even she seemed far away and inexplicably able to achieve what appeared to me to be miracles of confidence and initiative such as shopping and seeing to the children. I have lived then in blackness, grief, vulnerability, and despair. Time itself changed. The day went on for ever; the nights lasted for centuries. And yet I do not think that I once thought of killing myself. I was too much retarded. I remember trying to read. It would take me an hour to finish a line. And yet I recall nothing. I was able to sit almost motionless for hours. Actually, it was later — much later — when I was back at work and by then taking tablets and just about able to function that I took an overdose. One awful thing about my depression was the tremendous sense of guilt that I was unable to attach to any memory, or action or any part of myself. I was all feeling at that time and no thought — not real thinking, only a slow-motion kind of guilty rumination. Certainly, I had no hope that the future would bring me relief, let alone happiness.

The Experience of Depression,
pp. 269-279

MODEL 4: LEARNED HELPLESSNESS

The most well-known animal model of psychopathology is the "learned helplessness model," developed primarily by the University of Pennsylvania's Dr. Martin E. P. Seligman. In his initial experiment in 1967, Seligman electric-shocked dogs through a steel-grid floor with such intensity and persistence that the dogs stopped trying to get away and "gave up."[49] Since then, hundreds of investigators have developed their own learned helplessness models, including forcing animals to swim until they give up, or, in the language of the behaviorist, "learn to be helpless."[50-54]

Criterion 1: Uncontrollable aversive stimulation such as electric shock is just one proposed cause of depression according to a single theory of human depression: the learned helplessness theory. There are fully ten other well-known theories of depression each with its own postulated etiology.[55]

Many of the proposed causes of depression under other theories are virtually impossible to investigate in animals. For example, the learned helplessness model does not account for depressions caused by 1) loss of self-esteem, 2; loss of role status, or 3) loss of meaning of existence.[56]

In addition, learned helplessness theory fails to explain "success depression." When people finally reach a goal after years of striving — being promoted or getting a doctorate — many become depressed. This is precisely the opposite of what would be predicted by learned helplessness advocates, who claim that mastery over life events is the most powerful way to prevent depression.

Criterion 2: Learned helplessness in animals does not produce many of the symptoms of severe depression in human beings: insomnia, loss of appetite, guilt, suicidal behavior and ideas, and lasting mood changes. The most obvious difference between learned helplessness in animals and human depression is that experimental animals being subjected to uncontrollable electric shocks are extremely anxious, measured subjectively, behaviorally, and physiologically: they shake, quiver, defecate, screech, and urinate, some to the point of developing stomach ulcers.[57]

[49]M. E. P. Seligman, "Chronic Fear Produced by Unpredictable Shock," *Journal of Comparative and Physiological Psychology,* 66 (1968), pp. 402-411.

[50]J. Diner, *Physical and Mental Suffering of Experimental Animals* (Washington: Animal Welfare Institute, 1979), pp. 111-116.

[51]H. Anisman, L. Grimmer, J. Irwin, G. Remington, and L. Sklar, "Escape Performance After Inescapable Shock in Selectively Bred Lines of Mice: Response Maintenance and Catecholamine Activity," *Journal of Comparative and Physiological Psychology,* 93:2 (1979), pp. 229-241.

[52]R. L. Jackson, S. F. Maier, and D. J. Coon, "Long-Term Analgesic Effects of Inescapable Shock and Learned Helplessness," *Science,* 206 (1979), pp. 91-93.

[53]L. Kinney and J. Schmidt, Jr., "Effect of Cued and Uncued Inescapable Shock on Voluntary Alcohol Consumption in Rats," *Pharmacology, Biochemistry and Behavior,* 11 (1979), pp. 601-604.

[54]J. I. Telner and R. L. Singhal, "Effects of Nortriptyline Treatment on Learned Helplessness in the Rat" *Pharmacology Biochemistry and Behavior* 14 (1981), pp. 823-826.

[55]H. S. Akiskal and W. T. McKinney, "Overview of Recent Research in Depression" *Archives of General Psychiatry,* 32 (1975), pp. 285-301.

[56]*Ibid.,* p. 286

[57]J. M. Weiss, "Effects of Predictable and Unpredictable Shock on Development of Gastrointestinal Lesions in Rats", *Proceedings 76th Annual Convention American Psychological Association* (1968), pp. 263-264.

Criterion 3: The effects of three common therapies for depression have been investigated in learned helplessness models: 1) passage of time, 2) electro-convulsive shock, and 3) the antidepressant drug pargyline. The passage of time is effective in treating both depression and learned helplessness in animals.[58] Electro-convulsive therapy alleviates learned helplessness, but its effects on human depression are less clearcut. It probably alleviates certain cases of so-called "endogenous depression" (depression resulting from the person's internal psychological or physiological makeup), but its effects are unclear on "reactive depression" (depression resulting from external stress).[59] The antidepression drug pargyline appears to be effective against both learned helplessness and clinical depression of certain forms.[60]

CLINICAL IMPACT

It is unlikely that the animal learned helplessness models mimic any human condition whatever — except perhaps human beings under conditions of extreme physical stress. Dr. Dallas Pratt, Fellow of the American Psychiatric Association, writes:

> Surely these experimenters are contributing little or nothing to an understanding of the complexities of human anxiety or depressive states. If anything, these tortured and terrified dogs appear to be suffering from a traumatic reaction, similar to the soldier's "shell-shock", battle exhaustion or gross stress reaction occurring under circumstances in which men felt that physical destruction was inescapable.[61]

Yet, Pratt continues, there has already been extensive research on "learned helplessness" in human beings:

> Unfortunately, there has always been abundant human material of this sort available in our war-torn world, and no lack of publications on the subject. Kardiner's *Traumatic Neuroses of War,* for example, published as long ago as 1941 and an influential contribution to military psychiatry on the eve of the United States's entering World War II, was a penetrating study of acute anxiety in humans under stress.[62]

Out of the voluminous research on learned helplessness in animals, only a single potentially useful therapy has arisen for human depression. Drs. Seligman, Maier, and Geer found that forcible dragging "helpless" dogs from one side

[58]J. B. Overmier and N. E. P. Seligman, "Effects on Inescapable Shock Upon Subsequent Escape and Avoidance Responding," *Journal of Comparative and Physiological Psychology,* 63 (1967), pp. 23-33.

[59]T. R. Dorworth, "The Effect of Electroconvulsive Shock on Helplessness in Dogs," (Unpublished doctoral dissertation, University of Minnesota, 1971)

[60]J. M. Weiss, H. I. Glazer, and L. A. Poherecky, "Coping Behavior and Neurochemical Changes: An Alternative Explanation for the Original 'Learned Helplessness' Experiments." In: *Animal Models of Human Psychobiology,* G. Serban and A. Kling, eds. (New York: Plenum Press, 1976), pp. 141-173.

[61]D. Pratt, *Alternatives to Pain In Experiments on Animals,* (New York: Argus Archives, 1980), p. 68.

of the electric grid to the other — which was previously also electrified — showed the dogs that they *could* escape the shock and "cured" helplessness. The experimenters pulled three chronically helpless dogs back and forth across the shuttle box with long leashes to show the dogs that they could not escape the shock by going to the other side of the shuttle box.[63] Thus far, however, efforts to apply an analogous therapy in the clinic have failed to improve depression. Dr. I. Marks of the British Institute of Psychiatry, writes:

> The success experiences that overcome learned helplessness have not yet been proven practically useful for clinical depression. The therapeutic evidence so far is based on single case experiments and incompletely controlled group studies without significant follow-up differences at 36 months.[64]

In striking contrast, there are already a number of psychotherapies that were developed clinically that are effective in combatting the depressive's feelings of helplessness. In antidepression milieu therapy, for example, the patient is taunted to the point of emitting one of the most powerful emotions people have for controlling others: anger (as in the movie *Ordinary People*).[65] When this response is dragged out of his depleted emotional repertoire, the patient experiences an immeidate sense of power. The "cognitive therapies" are also designed to deal with the depressed person's feelings of helplessness. Dr. A. T. Beck, the pioneer of cognitive therapy, believes the primary task of the therapist is to change the negative expectations of the depressed patients to more optimistic ones. The aim is to change the patient from a negative "cognitive set" (i.e. "I am an ineffective person.") to a more positive cognitive set.[66]

The United Kingdom recently banned all learned helplessness experiments on animals.

[65]E. S. Taulbee and H. W. Wright, "A Psycho-Social-Behavioral Model for Therapeutic Intervention," In: *Current Topics in Clinical and Community Psychology III*, C. D. Spielberger, ed. (New York: Academic Press, 1971).

[66]A. T. Beck, "Cognitive Therapy: Nature and Relation to Behavior Therapy," *Behavior Therapy*, 1 (1970), pp. 184-200.

[63]M. E. P. Seligman, S. F. Maier, and J. Geer, "The Alleviation of Learned Helplessness in the Dog," *Journal of Abnormal Psychology*, 73 (1968), pp. 256-262.

[64]I. Marks, "Phobias and Obsessions," In: *Psychopathology: Experimental Models*, M. E. P. Seligman and J. D. Maser, eds. (San Francisco: W. H. Freeman and Co., 1977), p. 200.

MODEL 5: MOTHER-INFANT SEPARATION

Over the past 20 years, Dr. Harry F. Harlow and his associates at the University of Wisconsin have spearheaded efforts to develop a true "monkey model of human depression." The first monkey model to be developed by the Wisconsin team is the so-called "mother-infant separation model." In 1962, Drs. Seay, Hansen and Harlow reared infant rhesus monkeys with their mothers and peers for the first 6 months of life; then physically separated mothers from infants with a Plexiglass barrier for three weeks; finally, they reunited infants with their mothers. The results were dramatic: Infants responded to the separation immediately. They screeched, cried, tried to break through the Plexiglass barrier and eventually huddled in a corner of the cage, tightly hugging themselves.[67]

Criterion 1: It is highly unlikely that an infant monkey that has been separated from its mother can be used as a model for *adult* depression — even in monkeys, much less in human beings. The Wisconsin team's efforts to produce depression in older monkeys by social separation have failed utterly. For example, Drs. Bowden and McKinney housed monkeys over one year of age in pairs for six to eight months. The members of each pair were then physically and visually separated from each other for two weeks and then reunited. Although the monkeys responded to peer separation with active protest during the first few days, there was little indication of subsequent despair. They did not hug themselves and roll into a ball as the infant monkeys had done. Instead, the older monkeys acted normally after separation except for a slight increase in stereotypic rocking.[68]

In a second study, Drs. McKinney, Suomi, and Harlow studied the response of well-socialized adolescent monkeys to peer separations in 1972. The monkeys were 3-year-old males that had been reared with their mothers and peers for their first two years and then kept alone for their third year. Two groups of four monkeys were formed. Members of each group were permitted unlimited interactions with each other for four weeks. Then, members of one group were subjected to four repetitive separations, each for two weeks. The other group of monkeys was not separated during the study. As in the previous study, monkeys that were separated failed to show strong evidence of despair.[69] A third study of peer separation of juvenile-aged rhesus monkeys reported essentially the same findings.[70]

The negative results of the above studies left the Wisconsin workers themselves to reject the mother-infant separation syndrome as a model of adult human depression. Drs. McKinney, Suomi, and Harlow wrote:

> Our experimental understanding of separation reactions has been based almost exclusively on your organisms. In the case of humans most of the theorizing about separation effects with respect to de-

[67]B. M. Seay, E. W. Hansen and H. F. Harlow, "Mother-Infant Separation in the Rhesus Monkey," *Journal of Child Psychology and Psychiatry,* 3 (1962), pp. 123-132.

[68]D. Bowden and W. T. McKinney, "Behavioral Effects of Peer Separation, Isolation, and Reunion on Adolescent Male Rhesus Monkeys," *Developmental Psychobiology,* 5 (1972), pp. 353-362.

[69]W. T. McKinney, S. J. Suomi and H. F. Harlow, "Repetitive Peer Separation of Juvenile-age Rhesus Monkeys," *Archives of General Psychiatry,* 27 (1972), pp. 200-203.

[70]J. Erwin, J. Mobaldi, and G. Mitchell, "Separation of Rhesus Monkey Juveniles of the Same Sex," *Journal of Abnormal Psychology,* 78 (1971), pp. 134-139.

pression is based on observations of young children. Perhaps unfounded extrapolations have been made to more mature organisms. The presence of a biphasic response to separtion either in young animals or in young children in no way means that the same response will be seen at later developmental stages.[71]

Criterion 2: Though there are undoubtedly some people who hug themselves and roll up into a ball when depressed, such behavior is certainly not typical of most depressives.

Criterion 3: Data to date suggest that the antidepressant drug Imipramine is partially effective in reducing depressive behavior in monkeys.[72]

CLINICAL IMPACT

The mother-infant separation syndrome was well-known in human beings long before Dr. Harlow and his associates began their monkey studies. In the early 1940's, Dr. R. A. Spitz described the childhood emotional disturbance known as "anaclitic depression."[73] The Wisconsin team itself makes no claims to have made a "discovery" (i.e. a finding originally elucidated in work with animals that is later found to have applicability to human beings). One of the researchers, Dr. Stephen J. Suomi, writes:

Much of our primate research at Wisconsin is directed toward assessment of the physiological, social and cognitive capability of rhesus monkeys. We are not aware of human data — quite frankly, they tend to bias our research efforts. . . .[74]

One of the Wisconsin researchers' primary conclusions after completing the mother-infant separation experiments is that the distressed infant monkeys are yet another model of "learned helplessness." Dr. Harlow writes:

If we are to carefully examine those experimental separations in which a depressive reaction was exhibited as a consequence of the separation, certain consistencies appear. Each time, the monkey (a) loses a salient portion of its environment. . . . (b) has nothing in its separation environment that can replace what it lost through separation, and (c) has no power or ability to change its current social situation. In other words, depression results from social separation when the subject loses something of significance, has nothing with which to replace that loss, and is incapable of altering this predicament by its own actions. We might say that the subject in these situations is *helpless* and *hopeless,* and we can perhaps assume that it perceives its predicament.[75]

Rather than widening the understand-

[71]McKinney, Suomi, and Harlow, p. 202.
[72]H. F. Harlow and S. J. Suomi, "Primate Models of Depression." In: *Psychopathology: Experimental Models,* M. E. P. Seligman and J. D. Maser, eds. (San Francisco: W. H. Freeman Co. 1977), p. 147.
[73]R. A. Spitz, "Anaclitic Depression," *The*

Psychoanalytic Study of the Child, 2 (1946), pp. 313-347.
[74]S. J. Suomi, "Social Separation in Monkeys." In: *Animal Models in Human Psychobiology,* G. Serban and A. Kling, eds. (New York: Plenum Press, 1976), p. 24.
[75]Harlow and Suomi, p. 154.

ing of human depression, the mother-infant separation experiments merely mimic animal models that have already been intensively investigated (i.e. learned helplessness).

MODEL 6: VERTICAL CHAMBERING

In an apparent effort to create a living metaphor of human depression, the Wisconsin researchers put monkeys in a state of solitary confinement in a stainless steel V-shaped trough known as a "vertical chamber."[76] The scientists rationalized the experiment by writing:

> Depression has been characterized as embodying a state of helplessness and hopelessness, being sunken in a well for our monkey subjects, physically as well as psychologically. . . .[77]

Chambered monkeys usually spend the first day or two trying to escape, looking out through the steel bars covering the top of the cage. But the sides of the chamber are extremely slippery so most monkeys give up after a few days. Thereafter, they spend most of the time curled up in a ball at the bottom center of the chamber rocking back and forth.[78] *Criterion 1:* The researchers do not argue that most human depression is caused by solitary confinement. *Criterion 2:* The researchers do not argue that the symptoms shown by the isolate monkeys are similar to those in human depressives. The symptoms *are,* however, similar to childhood autism. Yet Dr. Harlow and his associates concede that the monkey isolate model probably does not model either depression *or* childhood autism:

> Some researchers have pointed out the similarity between elements of the isolate monkeys' behavior and specific behavior patterns exhibited by autistic human children. Anyone who has had the opportunity to observe both autistic children and isolate monkeys would feel compelled to consider them as

[76]S. J. Suomi and H. F. Harlow, "Apparatus Conceptualization for Psychopathological Research in Monkeys," *Behavior Research Methods and Instrumentation,* 1 (1969), pp. 247-250.

[77]H. F. Harlow and S. J. Suomi, "Production of Depressive Behavior in Young Monkeys," *Journal of Autism and Childhood Schizophrenia,* 1 (1971), p. 246.

[78]S. J. Suomi and H. F. Harlow, "Depressive Behavior in Young Monkeys Subjected to Vertical Chamber Confinement," *Journal of Comparative and Physiological Psychology,* 80 (1972), pp. 11-18.

examples of similar phenomena — particularly with respect to stereotypic rocking activities. Does this mean that, keeping in mind the basic behavioral differences between the species, the social isolation syndrome in monkeys serves as an effective model of childhood autism?

We doubt it. It is our belief that the social isolation syndrome in monkeys can serve as an adequate model for only one human disorder — the human total isolation syndrome. . . . If one could systematically separate human infants from mothers at birth and maintain them for the first two to four years in physical and visual isolation from other humans, the infants probably would exhibit the same reactions as monkeys reared in isolation.[79]

Criterion 3: Electroconvulsive therapy is one of the few clinical antidrepssion treatments so far tested on isolate monkeys; it proved of limited effectiveness. Harlow writes:

Results to date suggest that ECT is partially effective in reversing some depressive behavior. For example, chambered monkeys showed increased locomotor and exploratory activity following four weeks of thrice-weekly ECT. However, they did not exhibit substantial gains in social reactivity following shock treatments. Instead, they wandered about the test area apparently indifferent to the other monkeys sharing the test environment. When equivalent shock sessions were administered to socially normal control monkeys, their social interactions in the test environment also deteriorated, although their activity remained relatively constant.[80]

CLINICAL IMPACT

No potentially valuable strategies for treatment or prevention of depression have come out of the vertical chamber studies of monkey depression. Like the mother-infant separation model, the vertical chamber model is but another addition to the limitless arsenal of "learned helplessness paradigms." Harlow et al conclude:

The results of these various studies that employ a vertical chamber are generally supportive of a helplessness interpretation of monkey depression. The activities of subjects placed in the chambers are consistent with reports by other investigators of the behavior of nonprimate subjects placed in learned helplessness paradigms — for example, exposure to inescapable shock or noise.[81]

[79]Harlow and Suomi, "Primate Models." p. 145.

[80]*Ibid.*, p. 150.
[81]*Ibid.*, p. 160.

MODEL 7: NUCLEAR FAMILY SEPARATION

In an effort to simulate human depression more realistically, the Wisconsin team raised monkeys in a nuclear family — with fathers, mothers and siblings — and then separated them from their families later in life.[82-83]

Criterion 1: The researchers do not argue that most depressions are caused by separation from one's family.

Criterion 2: Mature monkeys that were separated from their families and then isolated, clapsed themselves as did infant monkeys that were separated from mother or peers or both. But self-clasping is probably extremely rare among adult human depressives.

Criterion 3: The author knows of no studies testing the effectiveness of antidepressant drugs on monkeys separated from their families.

CLINICAL IMPACT

Following a discussion of the nuclear family studies, rather than making an effort to clarify how or whether the nuclear family separation model could be used to understand human depression, Harlow and his colleagues go on to emphasize that other paradigms such as the use of inescapable shock should be vigorously pursued:

> We are confident that other techniques can be developed for production of depressive behavior in adolescent and adult rhesus monkeys. It is conceivable that procedures used to develop nonprimate models of depression might well yield depressive behavior in monkeys. For example, it is possible that if monkeys were subjected to inescapable shock, they

> might exhibit reactions that could be termed depressive. It would be interesting to see how similar such behaviors might be to those resulting from separation or vertical chambering.[84]

No potentially valuable strategies for treatment or prevention of depression have arisen from *any* of the many studies of monkey depression. The experiments have not in fact been designed to produce any such "discoveries," and are probably incapable of contributing to the understanding of human depression. The vast majority of Wisconsin's research has merely been an effort to validate the monkey models by demonstrating their ostensible similarity to human depression. In a recent review of a grant application to the Na-

[82]M. K. Harlow, "Nuclear Family Apparatus," *Behavior Research and Instrumentation,* 3 (1971), pp. 301-304.

[83]S. J. Suomi, C. J. Eisele, S. A. Grady, and H. T. Harlow, "Depression in Adult Monkeys Following Separation from Nuclear Family Environment," *Journal of Abnormal Psychology,* 84 (1975), pp. 576-578.

[84]Harlow and Suomi, "Primate Models," p. 165.

tional Institute of Mental Health from Dr. Stephen Suomi of the University of Wisconsin, Clinical Psychologist Dr. Kenneth J. Shapiro expressed a similar attitude toward the monkey model studies:

> The preponderance of the proposed research does not intend to advance knowledge, but rather to demonstrate that these conditions do induce depression, i.e. that they are indeed models. In its major thrust the research is not original in intent but duplicative of its earlier efforts and of similar findings in human clinical and experimental contexts. While "replication" is an acceptable function of research, costs of the research must take the fact of this limited function into account. Of course, the long range goal of the researchers is to generate advances through the model. The likelihood of such a contribution is indeterminate. Again, assessment of cost must "figure in" this indeterminacy. In my view, the likelihood of significant gains is small, for a number of reasons. (1) The phenomenon of interest is human depression. Purported depression induced in monkeys must be measured against that standard. While it is possible for the analogue to suggest a new lead, which we then "discover" in the phenomenon of interest, for the most part the models either confirm what is already known of this extensively studied phenomenon or they fail to serve as analogue, fail as a model. (2) The use of these animal models is "twice removed" from the phenomenon: First, the subjects are not humans; secondly, the animals are not themselves, i.e. they are themselves reared in artificial environments and subjected to artificial conditions. Any gain in precision and control is likely offset by losses through extrapolation across species and from artificial to natural environments and conditions.[85]

The Wisconsin researchers themselves apparently concede that there is no clear evidence that their monkey models have contributed to the understanding of human depression:

> . . . of what use are the data obtained from depressed monkeys for clinicians currently working with depressed patients? We have a considerably more difficult time establishing a strong case, (for such use) since so much monkey work to date has been based upon existing human data and theories. . . .[86]

[85]K. J. Shapiro, A review of the grant application MH 28485, entitled "Production and Alleviation of Depression" and submitted to the National Institute of Mental Health by Dr. Stephen Suomi of the University of Wisconsin. (At the request of Friends of Animals.)

[86]Harlow and Suomi, "Primate Models," p. 173.

PHOBIA AND OBSESSION

Rose Newcombe was a 32-year-old housewife, formerly a calculating machine operator and copy-typist. Since the birth of her third child three years previously she had had recurrent thoughts that, through her negligence, safety-pins might be lost in her baby's vagina, that she might drop a duster into a lavatory pan and use it, thus smearing furniture, that she might touch the genitals of men who were strangers, that she might say 'VD' in ordinary conversation and that she might push children in perambulators in front of traffic. Her anxiety had become such that she would telephone her husband, a stockbroker, to come home from his work twenty miles away or even drag at his coat begging him to say at home, when he was about to go to work. She regarded herself as depressed on account of her fears, which limited her life and made her much-loved husband unhappy. Unless questioned, however, she rarely complained of depression. All her spontaneous talk and innumerable notes, check lists, etc., written for herself and her husband, nurses and doctor, related to her search for reassurance that she had not allowed the things, of which she recurrently thought, to happen. She longed to go back 'before all this started' — i.e. before the end of her third pregnancy, through which she had felt very happy. She often seemed to picture her fears and compulsions as due to some 'outside force' which was not part of her normal personality; that was not truly an 'idea of influence'.

The patient's mother had been quarrelsome, untruthful and emotionally unstable. Sometimes she had been considerate and sometimes enraged over trivial matters. She had been excessively fussy over cleanliness and tidiness, shutting doors to the family once a room was clean. She had never been known to make anything — even a simple article of clothing. She had spent a great deal of time polishing her rings, of which she had several, and cleaning her teeth. She never actually wore any ring apart from her wedding ring.

The patient's father had been a coach-builder and died of stomach cancer three years before the birth of the third child. Usually placid and kind, he had been enraged occasionally to the point of physical violence by the mother's tantrums. The patient, who hated rows, had sometimes as a child pulled her parents apart.

— *Obsessional States,* p. 58.

MODEL 8: EXPERIMENTAL NEUROSIS, PHOBIAS AND OBSESSIONS

Since Ivan Pavlov observed a "neurotic breakdown" in a dog involved in the famous circle-ellipse experiment of Shenger-Krestovnika in 1921, researchers have driven laboratory animals to a state of "experimental neurosis".[87-89] The primary technique for inducing experimental neurosis is to put the animal in a situation of extreme internal conflict by, for example, pairing food with an electric shock.

Criterion 1: The experimental neurosis model postulates but one cause of human neurosis out of a number of possible causes according to various behavioral and psychoanalytical theories of neurosis. It is likely that experimental neurosis is only a model of those few human phobias that are caused by a specific traumatic experience in a particular situation such as a car crash. Beyond such instances, the model breaks down. Dr. I. Marks of the British Institute of Psychiatry writes that experimental neurosis fails to explain human neurosis even for the behaviorist.

A major problem encountered in conditioning experiments on fear acquisition is that clearly traumatic events — a definable US [naturally fear-inducing stimulus] — can rarely be pin-pointed at the start of human phobias and obsessions.... Because there is usually no history of a clearly traumatic onset to human phobias or obsessions, we cannot assume that they have been conditioned, only that they have

been acquired. Traumatic conditioning is uncommon in humans, and experiments on this issue are understandably rare.

In a typical animal experiment, a single CS [artificial stimulus] and a single US [natural stimulus] are arranged to produce fear. In contrast, a variety of situations usually trigger a patient's clinical distress, and those are seldom traceable to particular traumatic experiences. No one knows the original US, or if indeed one ever existed. The phobia or obsession simply appears, and search for the equivalent of unconditioned shock is fruitless.[90]

According to psychoanalytic theory, the model is even less satisfactory in accounting for the etiology of human neurosis. Among the first psychoanalysts to criticize the experimental neurosis model was Dr. Lawrence S. Kubie of Columbia University. In the 1939 meeting of the Harvey Cushing Society in New Haven, Connecticut, Kubie presented a paper in which he maintained that the model failed to account for the role of subconscious conflicting ideas in causing neurosis in man. The crux of the matter, according to Kubie, is that Koch's Postulates just don't work for mental illness:

The dream of the scientist in the field of psychiatry is to find an equivalent of Koch's postulates. His despair has been the impossibility of translating the voice and

[87]K. C. Corley, F. Shiel, H. F. Mauckl, L. S. Clark and J. H. Barber, "Myocardial Degeneration and Cardiac Arrest in Squirrel Monkeys: Physiological and Psychological Correlates," *Psychophysiology,* 14 (1977), pp. 322-328.

[88]D. C. Randall, M. P. Kaye, W. C. Randal, J. V. Brady, and K. H. Martin, "Response of Primate Heart to Emotional Stress Before and After Cardiac Denervation," *American Journal of Psychology,* 230 (1976), pp. 988-995.

[89]B. H. Natelson, A. Dubois, and F. J. Sodetz, "Effect of Multiple-Stress Procedures on Monkey, Gastric-duodenal Mucosa, Serum Gastrin, and Hydrogen Ion Kinetics," *American Journal of Digestive Diseases,* 22 (1977), pp. 888-897.

behavior of lower animals into anything comparable to the symbolic language of *Homo Sapiens.* This has limited the significance of efforts experimentally to produce neuroses in laboratory animals; because language is necessary for the communication of ideas, without which nothing comparable to a human neurosis is conceivable. In the human neurosis, whether it be an obsession, a compulsion, or a phobia, a seemingly diffuse or unfocussed state of anxiety or depression, or a conversion symptom, the disorder in conduct and feeling is merely the sign-language of a system of ideas, — which forms the nucleus of the neurosis, and which may in turn become the source and focus of secondary disturbing emotions. . . .

The experimentally induced disturbances in animals are quasi-neuroses, not in any true sense identical with human neuroses, — not unless we are to use this word to indicate something wholly different from that which the term means in human psychopathology. In the laboratory, what has been produced are primarily disorders of affects in the nature of more or less agitated depressive reactions and, although similar emotional states often occur in the course of neuroses, they arise as a product of the inhibitions and frustrations which result from the nuclear neurotic ideas and not as primary disturbances. In other words, more than one path can lead up the same mountain, and whereas a lower animal may be precipitated into a disturbed affective (emotional) state by being forcibly confronted in the laboratory with problems which he cannot solve, a human being creates his own insoluble dilemmas by coming under the domination of unconscious conflicting ideas and impulses which he can neither resolve nor escape.[91]

Criterion 2: Experimentally neurotic animals and human phobics react to the object of their phobia in a generally similar fashion. Both usually try to escape and experience such physiological changes as an increase in heart rate. To the extent that *obsessives* are afraid of the object of their obsession (e.g., dirt), the experimental neurosis parallels the clinical obsession. But most obsessive-compulsive symptoms are not seen in experimental neurosis. Obsessive-compulsive problems consist of obsessive thoughts or ruminations and compulsive rituals (which the patient realizes are silly but feels compelled to perform over and over). Obsessive thoughts can occur without rituals and vice versa. Usually, however, the patient ruminates and then performs the ritual. For example, a mother may repeatedly have the thought that she will kill her child and then compulsively search the house to make sure that she has gotten rid of all the knives.

Many other obsessive traits are absent in the animal model. Obsessives are often concerned with contaminating or harming themselves or other people. Some are terrified of going against some social taboo like swearing or making inappropriate sexual advances in public. Fears of contamination usually occur together with compulsive washing. Obsessives may feel contaminated each time they urinate, defecate, touch the floor, or pet a dog; they may then proceed to bathe for hours. Even bathing may not end the feeling of contamination. The obsessive may then disinfect all objects in the house. These and other "symptoms" are impossible to replicate in animals.[92]

Criterion 3: The testing of clinical antineurotic therapies on experimentally neurotic animals has been limited; except for the technique known as "counterconditioning," which appears to be effective in experimental neurosis and for certain human neuroses.

[90]I. Marks, pp. 204 & 207.
[91]L. S. Kubie, "The Experimental Induction of Neurotic Reactions in Man," *Yale Journal of Biology and Medicine,* 11 (1939), p. 541.

The development of effective therapies for phobics and obsessives are widely attributed to studies of experimental neurosis in animals. In particular, Dr. Joseph Wolpe of Temple University is credited with having founded a behavior therapy known as "counterconditioning" or "exposure *in vivo*." The subjects of his original experiments were animals that had been made neurotic by shocking them when they were presented food in a room where they had become accustomed to eating. In order to "counter condition" them, he would first feed the animals in a laboratory room only slightly similar to the one in which the shocks had been experienced; then in a somewhat more similar room, and then in one that was virtually identical with the original room. Eventually, the animals were able to eat in the training room without any visible signs of emotional upset.[93]

Notwithstanding the claims of some experimental psychologists, Wolpe's method was based on *human data* — a procedure first reported many years before in a study of children's fears by Mary Cover Jones in 1924.[94] Jones successfully used a technique in which children were given attractive food while a feared object was at some distance from them. The object was then progressively brought closer and closer to the child until it became a signal for food and hot a stimulus that evoked fear.

In fact, it is highly questionable that the technique called counterconditioning arose from anything more profound than common sense. The basic behavioral approach to treatment was enunciated clearly by John Locke over 300 years ago:

> If your child shrieks and runs away at the sight of a frog, let another catch it, and lay it down at a good distance from him; at first accustom him to look upon it; when he can do that, to come nearer to it, and see it leap without emotion; then to touch it lightly, when it is held fast in another's hand; and so on, until he can come to handle it as confidently as a butterly or a sparrow....[95]

It is clear that the immense amount of research on experimental neurosis in animals has only served to rationalize what was already known to be true in human beings. In another classic critique of the model, Dr. Howard F. Hunt of Columbia University wrote in 1964:

> Despite all this promise and appeal, the animal neurosis experiments seem not to have amplified our knowledge about human psychopathology materially. More characteristically, these experiments receive favorable attention because they illustrate, duplicate, or confirm things already known about the human case. While illustration and confirmation are not trivial contributions, we must ask why this comparative sterility.[96]

[92]I. Marks, pp. 208-209.

[93]J. Wolpe, *Psychotherapy by Reciprocal Inhibition,* Stanford University Press, 1958.

[94]M. C. Jones, "A Laboratory Study of Fear: The Case of Peter," *Pedagog, Sem.,* 31 (1924), pp. 308-315.

[95]J. Locke, *Some Thoughts Concerning Education,* (London: Ward, Lock & Co., 1693).

[96]H. F. Hunt, "Problems in the Interpretation of 'Experimental Neurosis,' " *Psychological Reports,* 15 (1964), p. 28.

ULCERS

As time went on, my doubts began to increase more and more. . . . I became more and more pessimistic. I was quite sure I hadn't passed. It sort of reached the climax the day they made the decision. . . . I just couldn't go over to the building and wait for the results. So I came home and nobody was there and I sort of paced the floor a bit. Then (another student) came in and told me that he had passed and I heard that (another student friend) had passed, and they began to persuade me to call up. I wouldn't call up and I was quite positive at the time that I had failed the whole business. I was very anxious and very upset. . . . Finally, about seven o'clock I decided to call up (a faculty member) and no one answered. So I went to the building around eight o'clock. I heard that he would be there. I was really completely shook up. It took about everything I could do just to walk up the stairs and go in. I was quite convinced that I had failed, and the thing that bothered me was that I tried rationalizing everything and saying that it really wasn't that important and that I could take them over again and so forth. . . . The thing that bothered me more than anything else was I thought I had failed, but it was a question of how I could accept the failure.

— Students Under Stress, p. 1

MODEL 9: PHYSICAL RESTRAINT

In an effort to clarify the psychological basis of ulcers in human beings, thousands of animals have been immobilized and subjected to extreme physical stress such as refrigeration and electric shock.[97-100]

[97]Diner, pp. 178-191.
[98]D. F. Wozniak and R. Goldstein, "Effect of Deprivation Duration and Prefeeding on Gastric Stress Erosions in the Rat," *Physiology and Behavior,* 24 (1980), pp. 231-235.
[99]W. P. Pare, B. H. Natelson, G. P. Vincent and K. E. Isom, "A Clinical Evaluation of Rats Dying in the Activity-Stress Ulcer Paradigm," *Physiology and Behavior,* 25 (1980), pp. 417-420.
[100]G. P. Vincent, W. P. Pare, and G. B. Glavin, "The Effects of Food Deprivation on Restraint Induced Gastric Erosions in the Rat," *Physiology and Behavior,* 25 (1980), pp. 727-730.

Criterion 1: No one argues that most human ulcers are caused by exposure to electric shock; situations that are stressful to human beings cannot be replicated in the laboratory. The only similarity between the etiology of human ulcers and animal "ulcers" is that both appear to be somehow related to stress.

Cirterion 2: One of the basic flaws in using animals to understand the human ulcer is that most animals do not get ulcers; they get a different gastric defect called a gastric erosion.[101] Gastric erosions in human beings are far more serious than ulcers. Erosions are not usually caused by stress as are ulcers; they usually arise from severe trauma such as burns, surgery or head injury. The bleeding from erosions is often so severe that the patient dies from loss of blood. Although psychological stress can occasionally contribute to the development of gastric erosions in man, erosions are usually caused by trauma.

Criterion 3: There is no clinical therapy that is specific for the particular psychological disturbance that often precedes and accompanies ulcers; thus criterion 3 is inapplicable.

CLINICAL IMPACT

The basic knowledge of the psychological causes of human ulcers comes from clinical studies conducted over a half-century ago. In 1931, Dr. Harvey Cushing, professor of surgery at Harvard Medical School, stated at the outset of his Balfour lecture:

> It is only in man that ulcers occur spontaneously with any considerable frequency and it is not at all improbable that the prevalence, particularly of duodenal ulcers, has something to do with the strain and stress of modern life; for people today rarely find it possible to enjoy the comparatively placid existence enjoyed by their forebears. All clinicians are familiar with the facts: (1) that "highly-strung" persons are particularly susceptible to "nervous indigestion" and associated ulcer; (2) that ulcers become symptomatically quiescent or even tend to heal when patients are mentally and physically at rest, and (3) that symptoms are prone to recur as soon as the victim of the disorder resumes his former tasks and responsibilities.[102]

Though subsequent animal studies were undertaken to clarify the causes of stress, such experiments have amounted to nothing more than an attempt to rationalize the original observations in human beings. Studies that utilize species that were found to respond in the human fashion are brought forth as support for the animal modelling approach, while studies involving those species that did not respond are ignored. It is well known, for example, that monkeys do not get chronic gastric erosions of any kind. For many years, the monkey was believed to be the ideal model of human stress-induced ulcers. The reason was the classic "executive monkey" studies performed by Dr. J. V. Brady and his associates.[103] Brady's

[101] J. M. Weiss, "Ulcers." In: *Psychopathology: Experimental Models,* M. E. P. Seligman and J. D. Maser, eds. (San Francisco: W. H. Freeman Co., 1977), p. 235.

[102] H. Cushing, "Peptic Ulcers and the Interbrain," *Surgery, Gynecology, and Obstetrics,* 55 (1932), pp. 1-34.

studies showed that monkeys that had to make more decisions were more likely to develop stomach ulcers. Yet not a single researcher has succeeded in duplicating Brady's findings.[104] In addition, experimental procedures that induce erosions in one group of rats will not always do it to another group. Dr. S. Bonfils and his associates have reported failures to find that struggling in restraint is consistently related to the development of lesions.[105]

[103]J. V. Brady, "Ulcers in 'Executive' Monkeys," *Scientific American,* Oct. 1958, pp. 95-100.

[104]B. Natelson, "The 'Executive' Monkey Revisited," (Paper presented at the Symposium on Nerves and the Gut. Philadelphia, Pennsylvania, August 1976. To be published in F. P. Brooks (Ed.), *Nerves and the Gut,* in press.)

[105]M. Dubrasquet, D. Sergent, M. Lewin, and S. Bonfils, "Relationship Between Circadian Rhythms, Spontaneous Activity, and Restraint Ulcer in the Rat." In: *Peptic Ulcer,* C. J. Pfeiffer, ed. (Philadelphia: Lippincott, 1971), pp. 105-112.

OBESITY

"Myra was the youngest in a professional family and had been considered normal as a child, bright and well-behaved. She had started gaining weight at menarche, when 12 years old, at about the same time her sister had begun to slim down. She did not appear unintelligent and had attended college on and off, but said, 'I am not committed to any course of learning.' She expressed the same attitude toward work and had done only the least difficult type of office work. Her previous psychiatrist felt that Myra's tendency to suspend reality to a rather striking degree had kept her 'uninvolved' in therapy. Myra spoke of the previous efforts: 'We had nothing to talk about,' but then she expressed resentment that 'He did not work a miracle; he did not give me will power.' Her whole attitude reflected extreme passivity and reluctance to make any effort herself. During the consultation she claimed to be unable to answer the simplest questions about the past. 'I can't picture myself at that age,' or, 'I can't remember anything about being in school.' She became somewhat more lively when describing areas of agreement with her parents, for example, being critical of others, such as her brother's and sister's spouses, but also of society in general. 'The Establishment,' and 'Washington.' It appeared obvious that nothing constructive could be accomplished as long as she spent her days alone in either her parents' or her sister's home, in charge of the food supply. Efforts to involve her parents were sabotaged by her with the claim that they objected to psychiatry."

— Eating Disorders, p. 159

MODEL 10: GENETIC OBESITY

Although the various animal models of obesity deal more directly with physical rather than psychological impairment, the following models were included in the book *Psychopathology: Experimental Models* and will therefore be considered as animal models of psychopathology.

In order to create an animal model of human obesity, animal researchers have developed inbred strains of mice that contain a genetic defect which causes them to become spontaneously obese from birth.

Criterion 1: There is very little evidence that human obesity is caused by an inherited metabolic defect. The author of the chapter on obesity in the book *Psychopathology: Experimental Models,* Dr. Judith Rodin, does not deny this:

> An understanding of animal models of genetic obesity may well provide significant clues towards classifying the biochemical and metabolic varieties of human obesity that at present defy our understanding, but for now there is very little evidence of a strong genetic endocrinological or metabolic dysfunction in human obesity. Genetically obese mice reflect metabolic forms of obesity, whereas human obesity seems to be more a problem of regulation. . . .[106]

Criterion 2: The author knows of no studies comparing the behavior of obese humans with genetically obese mice.

Criterion 3: Since there are so few true therapies that deal specifically with the psychological problems of the obese and virtually none that have been proven, Criterion 3 is inapplicable.

CLINICAL IMPACT

No new strategies for treatment or prevention of human obesity have arisen from the extensive studies of genetic obesity in animals. By and large, the research on inbred rodent obesity has been most useful in clarifying the differences between human and rat obesity. For example, what little evidence there is for a metabolic defect in human obesity indicates that it results in a failure to "burn off" food: to break down the chemical constituents of food and release energy (calories) in the form of heat. Whereas, in obese rodents, the defect appears to decrease the animals' ability to release calories (heat) that function to maintain body temperature in response to cold. Although a few studies apparently show that certain obese humans also fail to adjust their body temperature in response to cold, it is likely that the relatively large-sized well-insulated human being can maintain his body temperature without having to generate very much heat internally. During a symposium on animal models of obesity. Dr. W. P. T. James and his associates from the Dunn Clinical Nutrition Center in England presented a paper in which they said:

> it must be recognized, however, that acute cold stress is an unusual event in everyday life and that a failure of obese adults (human) to respond to cooling may reflect either the benefits of the additional insulation from the excess subcutaneous fat or, in cases where a fall in body temperature does occur in obese adults, an acquired defect rather than a primary abnormality. It must also be recognized that the proportion of energy turnover needed for the maintenance of body temperature declines in the larger

[106]J. Rodin, "Obesity." In: *Psychopathology: Experimental Models,* M. E. P. Seligman and J. D. Maser, eds. (San Francisco: W. H. Freeman Co., 1977), p. 50.

species from the level found in small animals, so that man may normally expend only a small fraction of his energy intake on maintaining body temperature. In addition, man adapts behaviourally to changes in environmental temperature not only by creating an artificial temperature in the home, but also by adjusting his micro-environment through changes in the clothing worn. . . .

In man, the dietary manifestation may predominate, with the thermoregulatory defect being the more important component in rodents. . . .[107]

MODEL 11: ENVIRONMENTAL OBESITY

Experimental psychologists attempt to investigate the role of various environmental factors in causing human obesity by subjecting laboratory animals to different environmental conditions. Drs. J. L. Knittle and J. Hirsch in 1968 attempted to examine the role of early nutrition in the subsequent development of obesity by allowing certain infant rats greater freedom of access to mother's milk. The rats were found to maintain a far higher number of fat cells throughout their lifespan than rats which were given more restricted access to mother's milk; no amount of dieting could reduce the number of fat cells in the "fat rats." Though the *size* of the fat cells could be reduced by dieting, the *number* could not. The authors concluded that obese people have particular difficulty taking weight off and *keeping it off,* because their huge reserve of fat cells are always just waiting to be "reinflated."[108]

Criterion 1: Knittle and Hirschs' belief that adult obesity is caused by overeating early in life and consequent "hypercellularity" is contradicted by a growing body of clinical evidence. Dr. W. P. T. James and his associates from Cambridge, England write:

> We have re-examined this problem in 125 patients and find little to support the current ideas on adi-

[107]W. P. T. James, M. J. Dauncey, R. T. Jung, P. S. Shetty and P. Trayhum, "Comparison of Genetic Models of Obesity in Animals," In: *Animal Models of Obesity,* M. F. W. Festing, ed. (London: MacMillan; New York: Oxford Univ. Press, 1979),

p. 230.

[108]J. L. Knittle and J. Hirsch, "Effect of Early Nutrition on the Development of Rat Epididymal Fat Pads: Cellularity and Metabolism," *Journal of Clinical Investigation,* 47 (1968), p. 2091.

pose tissue hyperplasia. Not only is the calculated number of adipocytes (fat cells) normal in most obese patients, but also there is no relationship between adipocyte number and the age of onset of the obesity. . . .[109]

Criterion 2: The author knows of no study examining the behavioral similarity between Knittle and Hirschs' obese rats and obese humans.

Criterion 3: Inapplicable.

CLINICAL IMPACT

No new modes of treatment or prevention of obesity have arisen from the study of environmental models of obesity. It was once thought that the Knittle-Hirsch study would shed light on the high recidivism rate among the obese: the frequency with which formerly obese people again became obese. A potential method of prevention would also have been suggested: conservative feeding of infants. But the findings of James et al cast doubt on the validity of the Knittle-Hirsch animal experiments for human beings.

MODEL 12: VENTROMEDIAL HYPOTHALMIC LESION-INDUCED OBESITY (VMH)

The third major animal model of human obesity is created by cutting the underside of the animals' hypothalmus: the region of the animal brain that controls appetite. The VMH model has become one of the most popular among animal researchers specializing in obesity.[110-111]

[109]James et. al., p. 234.

[110]J. Rodin and S. Schachter, eds., *Obese Humans and Rats* (Washington, D.C.: Erlbaum/Wiley, 1974).

[111]B. B. Lowell, G. N. Wade, J. M. Gray, R. M. Gold, and J. Petrulavage, "Adipose Tis-

Criterion 1: There is as yet no evidence that obese persons suffer from hypothalmic damage. Dr. Judith Rodin of Yale University, one of the pioneers of the VMH model, wrote in 1977:

> The striking parallels (in behavior) could be taken to suggest that something is awry with the hypothalmus of the obese humans. But although a few humans have specific anatomical or functional derangements, knowledge of such a condition is quite rare. . . .[112]

Criterion 2: Dr. Rodin and her associate Dr. Stanley Schachter argue that both obese humans and VMH rats are hypersensitive to environmental cues: mainly food. They further maintain that obese humans and VMH rats are *hypo*sensitive to cues emanating from within their bodies: i.e., a feeling of satiation. This hypersensitivity to environmental cues and hyposensitivity to internal cues has been called the "Internal-External Hypothesis of Obesity." Rodin and Schachter had claimed that the Internal-External dichotomy manifested itself in both obese humans and VMH rats in the following symptoms: 1) eating only tasty food, 2) eating fewer meals, but eating far more food far more quickly than normal, 3) being less active, 4) being hyperemotional (easily startled, excitable), 5) being better at avoiding painful stimuli, 6) being more sensitive to pain, and 7) eating large quantities of easily available food, but not usually working to get food.[113]

But there is very little evidence that obese humans and VMH rats are similar with respect to even a single behavior. Among the first to criticize the VMH model was Dr. Verne Cox, a Professor of Psychology at the University of Texas at Arlington. In a 1976 review of the book *Obese Humans and Rats* by Rodin and Schachter, Dr. Cox wrote:

> What is unconvincing about this book are the parellels that are drawn between the behavioral

characteristics of obese humans and VMH rats in what Schachter and Rodin believe to be analagous testing situations. These parallels lead Schachter and Rodin to speculate that the VMH may be implicated in some way in human obesity. The authors tallied animal and human studies that have outcomes in particular directions and assume that the more frequently reported outcome, when similar for animals and humans, reflects some behavioral characteristic common to obese humans and rats. Schachter and Rodin prefer this 'batting average' approach to attempts 'to reconcile or explain away incompatible findings.' In my view, numerosity is not a very useful measure of the validity of a particular scientific finding.

. . . In too many cases the data mustered in support of a behavioral parallel between obese humans and VMH rats are unconvincing or contradicted by more recent findings. One of the claimed parallels between obese humans and VMH rats is the ability to adjust subsequent food intake following liquid diet preloads. Schachter and Rodin claim that the available animal evidence is 'strongly suggestive but not conclusive.' They cite one animal study that employed solid food preloads and another study that employed only liquid diets, and conclude that 'Since these studies were done by different individuals and differed procedurally, it is clear that variables other than the liquid-solid one could account for the differential results.' I agree completely.

Another parellel offered by Schachter and Rodin is that obese humans, like obese VMH rats, eat less bad-tasting food than do their normal weight counterparts. All four of the cited animal studies indicate

---

sue Lipoprotein Lipase Activity in Rats With Obesity-Inducing Hypothalmic Knife Cuts," *Physiology and Behavior,* 25

(1980), pp. 113-116.
[112]Rodin, p. 61.
[113]Rodin and Schachter

this is true with regard to VMH rats. Two studies of obese humans are cited. One study is described as indicating that obese humans consume less unpalatable food than normal weight humans. The remaining study yielded no difference between obese and normal weight humans. The authors state that 'the data are more fragile than one would like but the trend for the two species is similar.' Trend? Thirty pages later this trend is listed among 'facts' that 'appear to hold for both the VMH-lesioned animal and the obese human.'[114]

The Internal-External Hypothesis of Obesity probably does not hold even for VMH rats. There is little factual evidence to support the view that VMH rats become obese because they are "hypersensitive to environmental cues." Cox continues:

> Both obese humans and VMH rats are described as hyperemotional and superior in active avoidance tasks when compared to their normal weight counterparts. However, these same characteristics are found in septal-lesioned rats and they do not become obese. Hyperemotionality and superior active avoidance learning are not necessarily indicants of hypersensitivity to salient stimuli that in turn leads to obesity. Powley has recently reported that vagotomy reduces obesity in the VMH rat but spares hypersensitivity to sensory aspects of food. The same surgery does not affect obesity following vagotomy even though vagotomy does not impair food intake to a degree that prevents obesity. Powley identifies hyperinsulinemia as the probable cause of obesity in the VMH rats and this strikes me as a more plausible explanation than hypersensitivity to salient environmental stimuli. In sum, I do not find the parallels drawn between obese humans and obese VMH rats very convincing. Nor does more recent evidence provide much support for the contention that hypersensitivity to salient stimuli accounts for obesity in VMH rats.[115]

Even more compelling is the fact that Dr. Rodin herself, one of the founders of the VMH model, challenged the validity of the Internal-External Hypothesis for *human beings* in the April 1981 issue of the journal *American Psychologist*. In a rare instance of scientific courage, Rodin proceeds to dismantle her own theory:

> ... The internal-external distinction is a widely held and cited framework used to explain differences between overweight and average weight persons, but this article challenges that application. Externality appears in persons of all weight categories and can lead to overeating in these individuals under specified conditions. But degree of weight gain and level of obesity depend on a variety of other factors. Moreover, the data suggest that internal sensitivity is not a unique characteristic of normal weight persons. Finally, the extreme separation of external and internal cues in the regulation of eating is not empirically supported [clinically]. External stimuli can be shown to directly influence internal physiological state, and a hypothesis regarding ways in which short-term internal signals may influence external cue salience can be tested. Thus, there is now considerable evidence challenging a simplistic internal-external dichotomy.[116]

Thus there is virtually no evidence to suggest that VMH-lesioned rats bear any behavioral similarity to obese human beings.

Criterion 3: Not applicable.

[114]V. Cox, "A Distracting Hypothesis," *Contemporary Psychology,* 21:1 (1976), pp. 3-4.
[115]*Ibid.,* p. 4.

[116]J. Rodin, "Current Status of the Internal-External Hypothesis for Obesity: What Went Wrong?" *American Psychologist,* 36:4, (1981), p. 361.

CLINICAL IMPACT

No advances in therapy or prevention of human obesity have resulted from research on Ventromedial Hypothalmic Lesion-induced obesity in rats.

MINIMAL BRAIN DYSFUNCTION (CHILDHOOD HYPERACTIVITY)

"This 6-year-old boy was referred because he was constantly in trouble at school as well as with his neighbors and with his own family. In kindergarten, he was observed to have very changeable moods, sometimes becoming extremely wild and violent, punching and poking other children, knocking them down and taking their toys; at other times, daydreaming, rocking back and forth passively. Occasionally, he would have a severe temper-outburst. Since infancy, he had been an overactive, nervous child, and a leader in the family when it came to making trouble. There were one older and two younger brothers, all three of whom eventually became patients for treatment of their hyperactivity; however, of the four children, this child was definitely the most difficult by far. He had a knack of provoking his father, who would then fly into a violent rage himself and beat him quite mercilessly. It would have been natural to have ascribed all his difficulties to the choatic and punitive environment at home."

— Minimal Brain Dysfunction, p. 113

MODEL 13: LEAD POISONING

One of the more widely-used animal models of Minimal Brain Dysfunction is developed by feeding lead acetate to pregnant mice and subsequently maintaining their offspring on a lead diet. The offspring are the putative models of childhood Minimal Brain Dysfunction.[117] *Criterion 1:* It was once thought that MBD might be caused by lead poisoning.[118] Today, there is little evidence to support such a view of the etiology of MBD.[119]

[117]E. K. Silbergeld and A. M. Goldberg, "Lead-induced Behavioral Dysfunction: An Animal Model for Hyperactivity," *Experimental Neurology,* 42 (1974), pp. 146-157.

Criterion 2: The lead-treated mice show only one symptom of the MBD "syndrome": hyperactivity. The onset of the dysfunction is very different in lead-treated mice and MBD children: MBD children are hyperactive *before* puberty, while lead-treated mice are hyperactive only *after* puberty.

Criterion 3: The drug amphetamine was long thought to be effective in calming MBD children. There is, however, little evidence that amphetamine calms MBD children.[120] Comparisons between the effects of clinical MBD treatments on MBD children and lead-treated mice are thus confounded by the lack of an effective clinical therapy. Nonetheless, amphetamine appears to sedate hyperactive lead-treated mice.[121]

CLINICAL IMPACT

No new strategies of treatment or prevention of MBD have arisen from the lead poisoning model.

[118]D. David, J. Clark and K. Voeller, "Lead and Hyperactivity," *Lancet,* 2 (1972), pp. 900-903.

[119]R. G. Lansdown, et. al., "Blood-Lead Levels, Behavior and Intelligence: A Population Study," *Lancet,* 1 (1974), pp. 538-541.

[120]L. A. Sroufe, "Drug Treatment of Children With Behavior Problems." In: *Review of Child Development Research,* F. Horowitz, ed. (Chicago: University of Chicago Press, 1975) Vol. 4.

[121]Silbergeld and Goldberg, p. 152.

MODEL 14: VIOLENT DOGS

Dr. Samuel A. Corson of the Ohio State University College of Medicine insists that his eight naturally-occurring, intractable, sometimes violent, mongrel dogs are models of Minimal Brain Dysfunction of childhood. Corson describes the original inspiration for studying MBD in dogs as follows:

> In the course of our attempts to characterize the psychobiologic nature of different types of dogs, we encountered a group of dogs which could not be trained at all in a Pavlovian stand, even before the introduction of any conditional or unconditional nociceptive stimuli. These dogs fought violently against the restraining Pavlovian-harness and tried to bite and chew everything within reach. Neither time nor patience was of any avail; in fact, many of these dogs became less manageable in repeated experimental sessions. . . .
>
> Because these dogs could not be conditioned (trained), our technicians referred to them as 'stupid,' just as teachers often refer to hyperkinetic children as being stupid. One had the impression that these animals could not filter information and could not narrow and focus their attention. This . . . suggested to us that we may be dealing with a syndrome comparable to childhood hyperkinesis. . . .[122]

Criterion 1: It is impossible to determine whether the dogs' hyperactivity is caused by the same factors that produce childhood MBD because the background of the dogs is entirely unknown (i.e., they are strays).

Criterion 2: This criterion is extremely difficult to assess because there is no true "MBD syndrome." The symptoms usually thought to be manifested in MBD children such as hyperactivity, distractability, learning difficulty, impulsivity, and poor peer relations, occur together in a single child diagnosed as MBD very rarely.[123] Nonetheless, the dogs exhibited only two symptoms that occur in the ostensible MBD "syndrome": hyperactivity and learning impairment. In addition, the animals displayed symptoms that do not usually occur in MBD children: extreme violence. As in the Lead Poisoning model, the dogs were hyperactive *after* puberty, while MBD is primarily a dysfunction of prepubescence.

Criterion 3: This criterion is difficult to apply for reasons indicated in the previous model. Nonetheless, MBD children do not respond to amphetamine in the same way as Corson's hyperkinetic dogs did. Those children who do become sedated by amphetamine, relapse as soon as the drug wears off. The dogs, in contrast, became permanently passive after amphetamine treatment.

[122]S. A. Corson, E. O'Leary Corson, L. E. Arnold and W. Knopp, "Animal Models of Violence and Hyperkenesis," In: *Animal Models of Human Psychobiology,* G. Serban and A. Kling, eds. (New York; Plenum Press, 1976), p. 117.

[123]J. S. Werry, "Studies on the Hyperactive Child: An Empirical Analysis of the Minimal Brain Dysfunction Syndrome," *Archives of General Psychiatry,* 19 (1968), pp. 9016.

CLINICAL IMPACT

No new strategies of treatment or prevention have arisen from the violent dog
model.

MODEL 15: NEONATAL SPLIT-BRAIN KITTEN

Dr. J. A. Sechzer and her associates contend that they have created an excellent model of Minimal Brain Dysfunction by destroying the corpus callosum — the band of fibers that connects the two sides of the brain (cerebral hemispheres) — of newborn kittens.[124]

Criterion 1: There is no evidence that MBD children have split brains. In fact, there is little evidence that MBD children have brain damage of any kind. Equally compelling is the fact that almost no children who are definitely brain-damaged also suffer from MBD. [125-130]

Criterion 2: Sechzers' kittens appear to suffer from all the behavioral deficits traditionally associated with MBD. Even if there were a single MBD syndrome characterized by these symptoms, the meaning of the kitten symptoms would be unclear. The reason is that lesions in a number of other areas of the mammalian brain (e.g., septal forebrain area, mammillothalamic tract, medial and lateral hypothalmus) also appear to cause the putative primary deficits in MBD: impaired learning and hyperactivity.[131-133]

Criterion 3: The drug amphetamine appears to improve the behavior of the Neonatal Split-Brain Kitten, but there is little evidence that amphetamine has a similar effect on "MBD" children.

[124]J. A. Sechzer, P. G. Kessler, S. E. Folstein, E. H. Geiger, and S. M. Meechan, "An Animal Model for the Minimal Brain Dysfunction Syndrome." In: *Mental Health in Children* (Vol. II), D. V. S. Sankar, ed. (New York: P. J. D. Publications, 1976).

[125]H. G. Birch, *Brain Damage in Children* (New York: Williams and Wilkins, 1964).

[126]S. Chess, "Diagnosis and Treatment of the Hyperactive Child," *New York State Journal of Medicine,* 60 (1960), pp. 2379-2385.

[127]G. S. Omen, "Genetic Issues in the Syndrome of Minimal Brain Dysfunction." In: *Minimal Cerebral Dysfunction in Children,* S. Walzer and P. Wolff, eds. (New York: Grune and Stratton, 1973).

[128]D. M. Ross and S. A. Ross, *Hyperactivity: Research, Theory and Action,* (New York: John Wiley, 1976).

[129]M. A. Stewart, F. N. Pitts, A. G. Craig, and W. Dieruf, "The Hyperactive Child Syndrome," *American Journal of Orthopsychiatry,* 36 (1966), pp. 861-867.

[130]J. S. Werry and R. L. Sprague, "Hyperactivity." In: *Symptoms of Psychopathology,* C. G. Costello (New York: John Wiley, 1970.)

[131]J. Brady and W. J. H. Nauta, "Subcortical Mechanisms in Emotional Behavior: Affective Changes Following Septal Forebrain Lesions in the Albino Rat," *Journal of Comparative and Physiological Psychology,* 46 (1953), pp. 339-346.

[132]E. E. Krieckhaus, "Decrements in Avoidance Behavior Following Mammillothalmic Tractotomy in Rats and Subsequent Recovery with d-amphetamine," *Journal of Comparative and Physiological Psychology,* 60 (1965), pp. 31-35.

[133]M. H. Sheard, J. B. Appel, and D. X. Freedman, "The Effect of Central Nervous System Lesions on Brain Monomines and Behavior," *Journal of Psychiatric Research,* 5 (1967), pp. 237-242.

CLINICAL IMPACT

No new strategies for the treatment or prevention of "Minimal Brain Dysfunction" have arisen from the use of animal models. The concept of MBD itself has outlived its usefulness. Children diagnosed as MBD suffer from a myriad of difficulties about which virtually nothing is known. The only key to progress against these childhood problems is painstaking research at the clinical level. In a book that challenges the MBD concept, two scientists urge that child psychologists start once again from scratch and examine all the various childhood disorders usually clumped under MBD with fresh eyes:

What is urgently needed is a more descriptive and operational class of definitions for these target children without any presumption as to etiology. Inferences should only be entertained on selected subgroups of the target children based on systematic behavioral, electrophysiological, and/or pharmacological measures. Only then will it be possible to move beyond a descriptive nomenclature....[134]

[134]H. E. Rie and E. D. Rie, eds., Handbook of *Minimal Brain Dysfunctions: A Critical View* (New York: Wiley, 1980), p. 674.

DRUG ADDICTION

"I started drinking socially and at parties and proms when I was about twenty years old. I didn't like it particularly at first, but I did like the effect I got from it. It made me feel quite grown-up and mature, and I think another added attraction was the fact that so far as my family was concerned it was forbidden, and it had a special attraction for that reason. After a while I really did enjoy drinking and what it did to me, and I became dependent upon it for every occasion. Eventually the day came when I was dependent upon it even when there wasn't any occasion. When I didn't have anything else to do — a dull evening at home — I'd sneak a few drinks upstairs in my room, and that began to be a habit.

In 1939, I went on my first week's bender of solitary drinking, locked up in a hotel room, because my family opposed my coming marriage. I figured that perhaps if I went ahead with that marriage, which I was sure was right for me, that would be the answer to my drinking problem. I thought I would be quite happy and never would I drink too much again. So — I tried that.

(I think my first feeling of fear came with my first week's solitary drinking, locked up in that hotel room. The hotel management, knowing that something was wrong, sent for a doctor. The doctor, apparently realizing that one thing that I certainly needed was sleep, left a bottle of sleeping pills there and in my drunken state I took them all, instead of the one or two he had prescribed. If it hadn't been for an alert hotel maid, I might have died then. From that time on, fear was with me because I realized that not only would I not remember what happened to me while I was drinking, but apparently I couldn't control what happened. And there didn't seem to be anything to do about it.)

Having passed over the border line, the next five years were filled with fear, failure and frustration. Tragedies during those years that were caused by my drinking, such as the breaking up of my marriage, the death of my child, other things — had little restraining effect. In fact, sometimes they served as good excuses to drink more, to forget. It was in Washington, D. C. that this transition took place, and that the really bad part of alcoholism began happening."

— Alcoholics Anonymous

MODEL 16: DRUG ADDICTION

Laboratory animals have been forced to become addicted to every conceivable drug including alcohol, opiates, barbituates, bromides, tranquilizers, amphetamines and nicotine in order to simulate human drug addiction. In a typical experiment, an animal is repeatedly injected with a drug via a "jugular cannula" (a narrow tube that inserts into the jugular vein) until physical dependence is established; then the animal is tested for its desire to voluntarily self-administer the drug by pressing a lever which results in an immediate infusion.[135-137]

Criterion 1: The fundamental flaw in all efforts to create an animal model of human drug addicts is that it is impossible to recreate in laboratory animals the addict's initial "motivation" for taking drugs. Many psychologists maintain that drug addicts begin using drugs because of emotional problems. People suffering from neurosis are thought to start taking drugs to relieve anxiety; psychopaths may take drugs to achieve a new thrill; depressives may use them to escape their depressed state. Some clinicians characterize all drug addicts as "schizoid, depressed, dependent, hostile, and sexually immature."[138] Opiate users have been described as people whose major anxieties are derived from difficulties with pain, sexuality, or aggression. It is speculated that alcoholics solve their sexual, aggressive, and dependency conflicts by drinking. In answering the question "Is an Animal Model of Alcoholism Possible?" Dr. T. J. Cicero said:

> The answer to this question is not simple, and, depending upon how one chooses to define alcoholism, there are many answers to it. If one asks whether there is a true model of human alcoholism, then the answer is no. That is, it is impossible using an animal to approximate those conditions which give rise to and maintain the abnormal consumption of alcohol in the human. Humans consume alcohol for a variety of psychosocial, and perhaps biological, reasons, some of which can be specified with some precision and others which have thus far eluded identification. Since we do not know why humans abuse alcohol, it is obviously impossible to have a true animal model of human alcoholism in the full sense of this condition. . . .[139]

In contrast, many experimental psychologists insist that the reasons people become addicted to drugs and the reasons laboratory animals become addicted are not fundamentally different. These experimentalists tend to "downplay" the severity of the emotional disturbance that often leads to drug addiction in an apparent effort to minimize the difference between the animal and human addict. Dr. Richard L. Solomon of the University of Pennsylvania, the

[135]Erikson, J. D. Sinclair and K. Kiianmaa, *Animal Models in Alcoholism Research* (New York: Academic Press, 1980).

[136]S. G. Beck and J. H. O'Brien, "Lethal Self-Administration of Morphine by Rats," *Physiology and Behavior,* 25 (1980), pp. 559-564.

[137]J. Bergman and C. E. Johanson, "The Effects of Electric Shock on Responding Maintained by Cocaine in Rhesus Monkeys," *Pharmacology, Biochemistry and Behavior,* 14 (1980), pp. 423-426.

[138]J. H. Jaffe, "Drug Addiction and Drug Abuse." In: *The Pharmacological Basis of Therapeutics* (3rd edition), E. Goodman and A. Gilman, eds. (New York: Macmillan, 1965), p. 286.

[139]T. J. Cicero, "Is an Animal Model of Alcoholism Possible? *Animal Models in Alcoholism Research,* K. Erikson, J. D. Sinclair and K. Kiianmaa. (New York: Academic Press, 1980), p. 100.

author of the chapter on animal models of drug addiction in the book *Psychopathology: Experimental Models,* writes that:

> . . . in addition to solving temporarily some social problems, the drug may relieve or reduce the unpleasantness of a variety of recurring emotional and motivational states . . .

The *degree* of emotional upset that leads to drug addiction in man, however, is relatively unimportant in assessing the validity of the animal model. The critical distinction between the laboratory model and the human addict is that people apparently become addicted for psychosocial reasons while animals are *forced* to enter the addictive cycle. The question of the degree of emotional difficulty that leads to addiction is but a "red herring" in terms of evaluating the animal models of drug addiction.

Criterion 2: The behavior of animals addicted to opiates (opium, laudanum, codeine, Percodan, Demerol, morphine, heroin, dilaudid, metopon, and methadone), in particular morphine, is generally similar to the human addict: both are so physically dependent that they will inject themselves with the substance and will undergo severe "withdrawal" symptoms without it. However, researchers have by and large failed to induce animals to become addicted to alcohol. Given a choice, animals will *not* consume alcohol, no matter how much they have been forced to consume previously.[140]

Criterion 3: Not applicable.

CLINICAL IMPACT

From the enormous amount of research on animal addicts, a theory has arisen which is supposedly useful for the prevention and treatment of drug addiction in human beings. Conceived primarily by Dr. Solomon, the "Opponent-Process Theory of Acquired Motivation," though defined in the extremely complex jargon of behavior theory, is basically very simple. In fact, it is so simple that it is virtually information-less. The theory holds that a drug addict becomes addicted because when he doesn't have drugs he craves them. According to the theory, the same holds true for a variety of "acquired motivations" such as love, sex and good food. Without love, grief ensues. Without sex-pleasure, sex-craving ensues. Without taste-pleasure taste-craving ensues.

In the same way, Solomon contends, without drug pleasure, drug-craving ensues. The authors of the theory hold that drug addiction is simply another "acquired motivation system of the opponent-process type."

The only "new" therapy suggested by the theory is already well-known: it is "cold turkey." Solomon writes:

> One deduction is painfully straightforward. Abrupt, involuntary withdrawal . . . should be optimal for obtaining the lowest possible levels of b-process magnitude and for weakening the b-process at the maximum rate.

The authors themselves imply the practical impotence of their theory.

Though the opponent-process theory of motivation suggests the

[140]N. K. Mello, "A Review of Methods to Induce Alcohol Addiction in Animals," *Pharmacology, Biochemistry, and Behavior,* 1 (1973), pp. 89-101.

means of preventing addiction, it also suggests that the grave difficulties in curing an addict are not necessarily due to our failure to find a good cure. Instead, the difficulties may be indigenous and normal for any opponent process system for affective and hedonic regulation.

(In other words, we have done nothing more than simply redefine drug addiction in elusive jargon without deepening the understanding of the addictive process.

CRITIQUE OF CRITERION 4: THE DOPAMINE HYPOTHESIS

No animal model could possibly meet Criterion 4 at present. The simple reason is that there is no direct evidence that any of the so-called "affective" illnesses such as depression and schizophrenia are caused by an underlying defect in the nervous system of human beings.[141-142] It is, of course, logically impossible to say that any animal model accurately mimics the neurobiological defect in the mentally ill without even knowing if such a defect exists.

Nevertheless, psychiatrists have attempted to elucidate the biological cause of mental illness by observing the effects of certain drugs on mental patients and then performing indepth pharmacological studies of the effects of those same drugs on the nervous system of animals. The theory that has dominated this research for the past quarter of a century is called "The Dopamine Hypothesis." It has been applied most widely to schizophrenia and depression.

The hypothesis states that schizophrenia is caused by an *excess* of certain neurotransmitters such as dopamine in the brain, while depression is caused by a *deficiency* of dopamine in the brain. The inspiration for the theory came from two accidental clinical observations in the mid-1950's. The first was that the treatment of high-blood-pressure patients with the drug reserpine produced a syndrome almost indistinguishable from clinical depression; the second was that the treatment of tuberculosis patients with the drug iproniazid led to euphoriant effects. When pharmacological studies on animals indicated that iproniazid *increased* the amount of dopamine within the central nervous system while reserpine *depleted* it, there began a massive investigation of the possible role that dopamine and other neurotransmitters (biogenic amines) might play in regulating mood and behavior.[143]

Today, however, few scientists still espouse the Dopamine Hypothesis. It has failed to predict innumerable drug effects on the mentally ill. The first major blow to the theory was the finding that reserpine did not cause true depression in either high-blood-pressure patients or healthy people. The reserpine-induced condition more closely resembled sedation and lethargy, or even cases of organic brain syndrome. The most clear-cut evidence that the reserpine-induced state is not depression was that drugs that could alleviate the pseudode-pression from reserpine — primarily the drug L-Dopa, a precursor of dopamine — could *not* improve patients with true depression. While the Dopamine Hypothesis would predict that the best way to treat depression would be to raise the patient's dopamine levels by treatment with L-dopa, most clinical studies have shown that L-dopa does not improve depressives and sometimes actually worsens their conditions.[144-146] Dr. Dennis L. Murphy, a clinical psychopharmacologist with the National Institute of Mental Health, discussed the results of the government studies with L-dopa at a recent symposium on animal models of psychopathology:

> To briefly summarize our data from studies of L-dopa, simply increasing brain catecholamines (e.g.

[141]S. H. Snyder, "The Dopamine Hypothesis of Schizophrenia: Focus on the Dopamine Receptor," *American Journal of Psychiatry,* 133 (1976), pp. 197-201.

[142]A. Carlsson, "Does Dopamine Have a Role in Schizophrenia," *Biological Psychiatry,* 13:1 (1978), 3-19.

[143]Maas, p. 1.

dopamine) by large oral doses of L-dopa, the amino-acid precursor of the catecholamines, was not found to be associated with striking antidepressant effects. Only 25% of the depressed patients improved, although it was of interest that it was principally one subgroup, patients exhibiting psychomotor retardation, who did improve, whereas none of the patients with the more anxious, agitated form of depressive symptoms improved. However, among the group of patients who did not improve, most were rated as exhibiting more over anger and irritability during DOPA administration. In addition, those depressed patients who had preexisting evidence of psychotic phenomena (principally depressive and paranoid delusions) as part of their depressive symptomatology were rated as more psychotic during the DOPA treatment period. Of particular interest was the development of hypomanic behavior in the subgroup of patients who had previous episodes of mania — the so-called bipolar patients.[147]

On the other hand, there are a number of clinical studies that show that schizophrenics who are being treated with drugs such as reserpine will *improve* if treated with L-dopa — precisely the opposite of what the theory would predict.[148] Many of the other clinical studies which contradict the dopamine hypothesis have been outlined in a recent article.[149]

Though the dopamine hypothesis has certainly served a valuable heuristic function, it has failed to explain any aspect of human psychopathology. No new therapies or preventive measures for psychopathology have been discovered from the immense amount of research that has been undertaken in pursuit of the neurobiological basis of mental illness. Dr. R. J. Baldessarini writes:

> Sadly, to date, they [amine hypotheses] have not led to a coherent basic biological theory of abnormal human behavior, nor have they led to the rational development of more powerful or safer therapies than those available nearly 20 years ago through the benefits of empiricism and simple good luck.[150]

In the same volume, Dr. Carroll continues:

> For some years the biogenic amine theory was considered a viable, potential framework for organizing our thinking and research strategies in this area. It is now 15 years since the theory was first outlined and we have not yet identified, in depressed patients, unequivocal and consistent, let alone unique physiological abnormalities which complement the pharmacologically derived amine theory. Without the theory we would not be where we are today in our understanding of depression: It has been extremely fruitful in generating many critical studies, at both the clinical and basic laboratory levels. Nevertheless, it has not proved to be very helpful to clinical psychiatrists and we should do well to consider it as no more than an indirect clue, vague and tenative, to help us be-

144F. K. Goodwin, D. L. Murphy, and H. K. H. Brodie, "Levodopa: Alternations In Behavior," *Clinical Pharmacology and Therapeutics,* 12 (1971), pp. 383-396.

145D. L. Murphy, F. K. Goodwin, and H. K. H. Brodie, "L-dopa Dopamine, and Hypomania," *American Journal of Psychiatry,* 130:1 (1973), pp. 79-82.

146J. Mendels, J. L. Stinnett, and D. Burns, "Amine Precursors and Depression," *Archives of General Psychiatry,* 32 (1975), pp. 22-30.

147Murphy, p. 269.

148H. Y. Meltzer, and S. M. Stahl, "The Dopamine Hypothesis of Schizophrenia: A Review," *Schizophrenia Bulletin,* 2 (1976), pp. 19-76.

149M. Alpert and A. J. Freidhoff, "An Undopamine Hypothesis of Schizophrenia," *Schizophrenia Bulletin,* 6:3 (1980), pp. 387-390.

150Baldessarini, "Amine Hypotheses," p. 72.

gin our investigations.

I regard it as a healthy sign that we are now beginning to examine the theory in a critical way because that implies that maybe we feel able to discard the theory without too much anxiety over what to replace it with. In its original form the theory has outlived its usefulness and we will be submitting ourselves to a restrictive orthodoxy if we rely on it exclusively for our future research strategies.[151]

[151]Carroll, "Clinical Research Strategies," In: *The Psychobiology of Depression,* J. Mendels, ed. (New York: Spedtrum Publishing, 1975), p. 146.

CONCLUSION

The legacy of Koch's postulates aproaches a dead end. Despite the proclamations of contemporary experimental psychologists, there is no evidence that the classic "animal models of psychopathology" have improved the mental health of a single human being. The animal models themselves are but the dimmest reflection of the human disorders. Not a particle of knowledge from animal experimentation has illuminated either the psychological or biological basis of mental illness. Since the animal modelling technique has proved virtually useless against the bonafide chronic noninfectious diseases including cancer, it is extremely unlikely that animal research will ever prove to be of value to clinical psychologists. The multi-million dollar expenditures for psychological experiments on animals are clearly a gross waste of taxpayer revenue.

It is perhaps illuminating that the earliest experimental psychologists — Wundt, Titchener and Kulpe — chose to focus entirely on human subjects. Pavlov came later. Though the idea of using animals to study human psychopathology appealed to some experimental psychologists of the time, most continued to restrict their research to human beings. To this day, the vast majority of psychological studies are conducted with human subjects. A recent survey of the 1939 and 1979 volumes of the *Psychological Abstracts* reveals that only 9.97% of the 1939 involved animals and even fewer — 7.47% — were performed on animals in 1979.[152] Rather than being a mainstay of psychological research, the animal model approach is more accurately viewed as a digression from the main body of contemporary psychology.

Most psychologists have evidently long been aware of the precariousness of extrapolating the results of animal experiments to man. It is no coincidence that all of the clinically — useful antipsychotic drugs were discovered from their effects on people: Had these drugs first been tested on animals, many would have been altogether discarded. In fact, every advance in the treatment of psychopathology — from behavior therapy to antidepression milieu — was developed not from laboratory research but through an intimate understanding of the human situation.

Despite the author's adamant pronouncements, doubt assuredly lingers in the reader's mind. Indeed, the intuitive appeal of using animals to study human psychopathology is difficult to resist. Nonetheless, though basic similarities between species allow scientists to draw valid conclusions about certain fundamental physiological, anatomical and behavioral characteristics (e.g., "classical conditioning"), the differences between species confound interspecies extrapolation as investigators move from the general to the specific.

Not surprisingly, there are experimental psychologists who insist that animal models *can* be used to answer highly specific questions about human psychology. Not only is such a contention false *a priori* (it is logically impossible for an experiment on something other than the subject of interest to provide definitive data for the actual subject), but it is usually proven false after careful examination of the clinical evidence. A case in point is the world-renowned study of infant love performed by Dr. Harry F. Harlow and his associates at the University of Wisconsin. In 1958,

---

[152]Gallup and Suarez, p. 211.

Harlow set about the task of proving that all the Freudian and behaviorist theorists who studied human beings were wrong about the reason a human infant loves its mother. While the human theorists maintained that human infants grow to love mother because their hunger is alleviated whenever they have contact with the breast, Harlow believed that the only reason infants love their mother is body contact itself. To prove his point, he performed an experiment on rhesus monkeys: Two artificial mother surrogates were created, one cloth-covered and the other made of wire mesh. For half the experimental period, the cloth surrogate had a milk nipple attached to it, while during the rest of the experiment the wire mother equipped with a milk nipple. The infant monkey was allowed to choose either surrogate at any time during the experiment. The results were unambiguous: The infant monkey continuously clasped and clung to the cloth mother whether or not it had milk.[153] In Harlow's mind, his thesis had been proven: maternal contact is far more important than feeding in establishing the infant-mother bond. He went so far as to claim:

> The data of the human theorists did not generalize to monkeys because the human theory was false. Monkey theories basically generalized to human infants because the monkey facts were true. . . .
> Sometimes when monkey data fail to generalize to human data the answer lies in the superiority of the monkey data and the need to revise those data that are human. . . .[154]

Few quotations so exemplify the magnitude of the impact of Koch's postulates and the long-standing bias against clinical and epidemiological data that they engendered.[155] Harlow's assertion, however, has no basis in either logic or fact. It clearly goes beyond the bounds of logic to suggest that human data is inferior to monkey data when the subject of interest is a human being. Understandably, many psychologists have criticized the original Harlow study because of the evidence that contact comfort is far more important for monkey infants than for human babies. Clinical psychologist Dallas Pratt scoffs, "It has been pointed out that contact comfort is *more* important in monkeys than in man, and anyone who has watched an infant monkey clinging tightly to its mother as the latter swings through the trees can easily understand why."[156] (In a very real sense, the apparent quest to reveal "true man" through monkey experimentation is symptomatic of an identity crisis rather than scientific progress.)

Notwithstanding the fact that animal models can be used to confirm certain basics of human behavior, it is unlikely that they will ever lead to significant clinical advances in psycho-pathology. While animal psychology may be qualitatively similar to human psychology, the two are often *quantitatively* eons removed. If experimental psychologists are to develop truly predictive models of human psychopathology, they might recall that the idea of a "model system" was borrowed from the "exact" sciences. One of the basic tenets of such sciences is that *the usefulness of a model depends on its specificity.*[157] While models that describe the real world loosely may be of academic interest, only simulations that are extremely precise provide the kind of insight that is necessary to take action to

[153]H. F. Harlow and R. R. Zimmerman, "The Development of Affectional Responses in Infant Monkeys," *Proceedings of the American Philosophical Society,* 102 (1958), pp. 501-509.

[154]H. F. Harlow, J. P. Gluck, and S. J. Suomi, "Generalization of Behavioral Data Between Nonhuman and Human Animals," *American Psychologist,* August 1972, pp. 709-716.

[155]Peller, *Quantitative Research.*

[156]Pratt, p. 61.

[157]I. D. J. Bross, "Scientific Strategies in Human Affairs: Use of Deep Mathematical Models," *Transactions of the New York Academy of Sciences,* 34 (1972), pp. 187-199.

protect the public health or to send rockets screaming through outer space. Plato puts it in a nutshell:

A cautious man should above all be on his guard against resemblances; they are a very slippery sort of thing.[158]

[158]Plato, "The Sophist," translated by F. M. Cornford (Plato's Theory of Knowledge, London, 1935, p. 180).

BIBLIOGRAPHY

1. *Alcoholics Anonymous,* New York, Alcoholics Anonymous World Services, Inc., 1955.

2. Beech, H. R., *Obsessional States,* London, Methuen & Co. Ltd., 1974.

3. Bruch, H., *Eating Disorders,* New York, Basic Books, Inc., 1973.

4. Fann, W. E., Karacan, I., Pokorny, A. D., Williams, R. L., *Phenomenology and Treatment of Depression,* New York, Spectrum Publishing, 1977.

5. Garret, H.E., *Great Experiments in Psychology,* New York, Appleton-Century-Crofts, Inc., 1951.

6. Gross, M.D. and W. C. Wilson, *Minimal Brain Dysfunction,* New York, Brunner/Mazel Publishers, 1974.

7. Mechanic, D., *Students Under Stress: A Study in the Social Psychology of Adaption,* New York, The Free Press of Glencoe, 1962.

8. Rowe, D., *The Experience of Depression,* New York, John Wiley & Sons, 1978.

9. Sechehaye, M., *Autobiography of a Schizophrenic Girl,* New York, Grune and Stratton, Inc., 1951.

10. Wolman, B. B., *Contemporary Theories and Systems in Psychology,* New York, Plenum Press, 1981.

DATE D